CONTEMPORARY COMMUNITY HEALTH SERIES

THE DOCTOR TREE

Ralph N. Zabarenko
Lucy M. Zabarenko

THE DOCTOR TREE

Developmental Stages in the Growth of Physicians

University of Pittsburgh Press

Published by the University of Pittsburgh Press, Pittsburgh, Pa., 15260
Copyright © 1978, University of Pittsburgh Press
Feffer & Simons, Inc., London
Manufactured in the United States of America

Library of Congress Cataloging in Publication Data

Zabarenko, Ralph N.
  The doctor tree.

  (Contemporary community health series)
  Bibliography: p. 171
  1. Medical education—Psychological aspects.
2. Medical students—Psychology. 3. Physicians—
Psychology. I. Zabarenko, Lucy M., joint author.
II. Title. III. Series. [DNLM: 1. Physicians.
W21 Z12d]
R737.Z3   610'.7'3   77-18340
ISBN 0-8229-3370-5

Publication of this volume
was supported by a grant
from Staunton Farm.

As promised, to M. R., Debby, Leah, and Judy

Contents

Preface

This book presents the thoughts and ideas of two born doctor-watchers forced to become writers by the compelling nature of their subject matter. Both of us were reared in large, close-knit families in which teachers, scholars, artists, but especially doctors were important figures. Intimacy as well as crowding provided ample opportunity for curious children to explore the possibilities of identification, admiration, rejection, and loathing, and eventually to become fascinated with the whole field of medicine.

The work we describe had its roots in the decades we spent in teaching and research at the Staunton Clinic, University of Pittsburgh Medical School. We have drawn freely upon our own experiences and those of our colleagues; each of the vignettes reported in the text is taken from real life. But diligent effort has gone into eradicating as many of the needlessly identifying details as is compatible with having the picture remain intact. What we have in mind, to pursue the visual analogy, is neither a photograph nor an impressionistic image, but a line drawing. If, in these line drawings, our patients, students, or colleagues fancy they see themselves, we encourage them to pause, look again to be certain, and then consider how well the same line drawing might fit incidents from their own observations. That, after all, is our main purpose.

The Rockford School of Medicine, University of Illinois College of Medicine, provided many resources which made the writing possible. The assistance of the staff of the Crawford Medical Library at the Rockford School of Medicine was truly invaluable. Of the many people whose assistance was indispensable we owe a special debt to

Mr. and Mrs. George B. Craig, Jr., whose interest in our work was heartening and especially welcome in its constancy over many years. We are also grateful to Merton Gill, M.D., whose careful reading of the manuscript in an early phase sent it back to the drawing board when that was what was needed; to C. H. William Ruhe, M.D., and his staff at the American Medical Association who encouraged us to continue at a low point; and to Mr. Frederick A. Hetzel of the University of Pittsburgh Press whose willingness to look at the manuscript came at a time when it was on the brink of being abandoned.

The eloquent articulation, by William Grove, M.D., Vice Chancellor for Academic Affairs at the University of Illinois, of the need for research in this area sparked the beginning of our work. It was further encouraged by Robert L. Evans, M.D., former Dean of the Rockford School of Medicine, who urged us to think of it as a charge. And finally, to Miki Metzger and Mimi Hartsfield who typed innumerable drafts, served as friendly critics, editors-in-residence, and general support in the profoundest sense, our most sincere gratitude.

THE DOCTOR TREE

CHAPTER 1

Beginnings

Sometimes vigilant observation yields one episode that captures, as though in amber, a specimen of what is to be the focus for lengthy study. Preserved and undamaged, so that each detail is accessible, it can be examined at leisure, looked at in different lights, with varied degrees of magnification, and within the perspective of mounting information. The following story is that sort of find.

On a summer Saturday in 1965 a couple in their late sixties were brought to the emergency room of a general hospital by the police after an automobile accident in which their car had collided with the rear of another. The hospital was one of ten comprising a medical center, staffed and operated under the auspices of a large urban medical school of good repute. The first physician they encountered was the emergency room resident. He diagnosed the driver as suffering from bruises of the chest and discharged him. The passenger was not so fortunate. Upon inquiring, she discovered that the internist who usually cared for the couple was out of town. A general surgeon, however, one who usually worked with the internist and who was familiar with the patient, was able to see her. A routine chest x-ray and x-rays of her head and abdomen were taken. The patient complained to the surgeon of pain in her right arm, now badly swollen four hours after the accident. He palpated the arm, told her that it was a hematoma and would go away in a few days. Though intelligent and well informed, she didn't know exactly what a hematoma was, but by this time she was in considerable pain and feeling weak. She had in fact, nearly fainted twice during the x-ray procedures. She was also acutely aware that the surgeon had been called away from a tennis tournament in which he was playing to see her. For these reasons and others she did not ask what a hematoma was nor did she request any medicine for the pain, and none was given. This was her last contact with the surgeon.

After another hour she was seen by a doctor who introduced himself as an oral surgeon. He examined her and explained that he had seen the x-rays, that her broken jaw would require surgery, and that she would probably lose some teeth. But these procedures would have to wait until the next week. Further tests were needed, and it was important that she rest from the trauma of the accident. Since he seemed less rushed than the other doctors, she was able to ask him about the x-rays and tell him she wanted something to ease her pain. He reassured her that there were no other fractures that he could see, and no signs of internal injuries, but emphasized that hospitalization was important so that she could be "watched carefully." He appeared dismayed and surprised that she had had no medication for pain and said he would order it. Emboldened somewhat, the woman showed this man her arm, pointing out it had not been x-rayed. The conversation, until then comforting and relatively relaxed, crunched to a stop. The doctor, with a tone which implied she ought to have known, said briskly that the arm was not in his area.

The following Tuesday the fractured jaw was set and wired, and several teeth were removed. The surgery went well, but the patient was still complaining about her arm, now much less swollen and obviously deformed. Her children explained what a hematoma was and that it might take a little more time to absorb. On Wednesday she was visited socially by a physician friend who was on the hospital staff. At the patient's and family's (rather shamefaced) request, this doctor ordered an x-ray of the arm as a favor, to comfort and satisfy everyone. The x-ray was taken on Thursday. A fracture was plainly visible, but the x-ray was not officially "read" at once. Some time was taken to contact an orthopedic surgeon and ask him to consult on the case. By Saturday noon, one week after the accident, a broken arm had not yet been officially diagnosed nor treatment begun.

This account is factual, the result of firsthand information. Unhappily, similar medical horror stories could be elicited from many patients. It is not sufficient or useful just to cluck our tongues or even to note that a decade later things might have been different—a malpractice suit and settlement might have been involved or better care might have been provided. The fact is that a fractured arm, capable of being recognized by many nonphysicians, diagnosed by many nurses and all veterinarians, had gone undetected in a large, well-equipped, urban hospital, staffed by a faculty of a university medical school. How can such a thing happen?

The answer, so readily apparent in this example, cannot be proclaimed too often: There was no coordination of treatment because the primary-care physician—the familiar internist—was absent. No one had attempted to substitute for him, and thus what has come to be called the "medical care system" had operated on a kind of automatic pilot, functioning within professionally and institutionally sanctioned channels. Each physician had discharged the duties of his realm honestly and well, though some might fault the general surgeon. The nursing staff was concerned, and rightly so, with carrying out familiar pre- and postoperative procedures. The patient's complaints of pain in her arm were duly recorded, but the chart indicated that it had been diagnosed. It is not common for a nurse to question a physician's diagnosis. In this case there was no one in charge to whom to bring the evidence, and the patient was not inclined to make a fuss—for a while. The hospital staff, then, had done their jobs *as they saw them* and indeed as they are defined by the whole medical care conglomerate. The absence of a primary-care physician was not felt to be important enough to remedy, even by the patient. In fact, she and her family had contributed to her neglect by accepting without question the surgeon's tentative diagnosis and continuing to consider it correct even in the face of mounting evidence that it was not. The system's operation had in some ways been a success, but the patient had gone in part untreated.

We and many others have vexed ourselves for some time with the nagging unpleasantness of trying to understand how such things happen. The more we have studied, the more it has become clear what a complicated function adequate medical care is. Simplistic concepts or heated partisan positions cannot explain the data, unless one is willing to settle for the superficial or the derogatory. Malpractice suits may alert medical practitioners to existing deficiencies, but will not supply many clues about how to fix them. Nor can a frontal legislative assault on the maldistribution or shortage of doctors produce lasting change. One of our proposals will be that failures in medical care represent the end results of the developmental processes we shall be discussing. There is also a complex and involved interaction between the medical profession and the culture it serves.

Physicians are foremost among those who would like to eradicate the possibility of episodes like the one we have described. But if the methods used to monitor and improve medical care have not yet produced the kinds of change society requires, it may be that an entirely new approach is needed, a fresh search for what needs to be changed and how best and most surely this can be accomplished. Perhaps it is time to look not at how the system functions but how the individual doctor grows.

The medical schools which provide physicians their basic technical training and inculcate the attitudes and behaviors which will characterize their professional lives are plagued by substantive problems. Competition for admission to these schools has become increasingly fierce; some students say it is brutalizing. Those who must set criteria and make judgments—administrative officials, admissions officers, and committees—can find little comfort in the enormity of the task or the profession's track record. Consider, first, the sheer numbers involved. In some American medical schools there may be as many as fifty applications for each place available. Most often a number of standard measures are applied to eliminate the unlikely, including undergraduate grades and scores on standardized written tests, for example, the Medical College Admissions Test. These numbers are usually weighted to take into account each medical school's particular emphasis and the undergraduate institutions' standards. The result is a smaller, selected number of possible students with specific characteristics. Where interviews are used, further selection takes place.

These procedures are sensible and valid, but, unfortunately, not sufficient to the task. The difficulty of the issues involved and the plight of those who must cope with them are best exemplified by the discouragement of one medical school dean. He remarked that even after all known measures were used to reduce the number of applicants, there remained in his school ten fully qualified applicants for each place. Reviewing the results of past selections, he concluded that the final choice might be made just as successfully by using a table of random numbers. In this kind of despair we have heard a plea for help. And it is another reason for the work that we shall present.

One point is abundantly clear: Many young people can meet conventional and valid standards of intellectual ability for medical studies, but a growing volume of data suggests that these measures do not specify well enough whether the students will successfully complete medical school or be competent physicians if they do graduate. As the storm of protest from consumers of medical care has increased, the conviction has deepened in most medical educators that (1) it takes more than intelligence alone to be a good physician, and (2) better measures of the potential for the other attributes involved in physicianhood are urgently needed to improve admissions procedures, teaching, and eventually patient care.

For those who are looked after by doctors, which includes almost all of us, and for those who educate doctors, the best hope lies in abandoning any expectation of quick or easy solutions. These are apt to produce at best temporary improvement. They may induce slight shifts which result in no substantial change, and at worst, they may delay appreciating and grappling with the magnitude and depth of the problems.

Before going further we want to explain where our searches have led us, to present our credentials and the experiences that generated the ideas. The accumulation of data upon which we will draw has grown slowly, almost incidentally, from many kinds of work. Following the currents of our curiosity in a vast delta of encounters with physicians, we have discovered some things which seem worth saying. But this kind of a search means that large areas are necessarily unexplored.

We begin then by stating what we will not discuss. The overlapping domains designated by terms like *delivery of medical care* or *health-care systems* are distinct areas of expertise. They include medical sociology, medical anthropology, systems theory and its application, and the study of institutions—how they function or malfunction, at what fiscal and personal cost, and with what effect. These topics we leave to qualified specialists. Any reader interested in them can now find more literature at any level of complexity than can be mastered easily in a short time.

Our interests have fastened upon understanding the physician. The reasons are many: As teachers we have worked at many levels of medical education, from premedical undergraduates, through medical students, residents, and physicians who have been in practice from five to thirty years. We have used lectures, special seminars, hospital rounds, and spontaneously occurring clinical material to do the teaching. If this list sounds scattered or grandiose, it is because when instructing at different maturational points and trying to take decent account of the special qualities in each learner, one needs to have at hand every possible strategy. Without the capacity for versatility the opportunities for effective teaching constrict, and the target within the learner, or even the learner himself, may be swiftly out of range. And as always, the bargain has been uneven. Our students have taught us more than we have ever given them. It is in partial payment of this debt that we have felt obligated to try to make sense of what they have taught us, to share it and use it as a force for better teaching.

As researchers, we have made physicians the object of study. Their generosity in permitting this must be accounted a credit to them, for it is not easy to endure such scrutiny no matter what the guarantees of anonymity, scientific merit, or kindly predisposition in the observers. Accordingly, the incessant mining of the resultant data is mandatory. None of the efforts of the research or the forebearance of its doctor-subjects must be wasted; no assumption made hastily that any reservoir of information has been sufficiently reexamined. As psychoanalysts treating physicians and their families, we have seen through a different lens another universe in the space of what it means to be a physician and to live and work with healers.

Finally, we would be less than candid if we did not acknowledge the influence of personal experiences. Both of us were reared in large, close-knit families where physicians were important figures. Like most other people born in the first third of the twentieth century, encounters with doctors loomed as vivid parts of preschool experiences with illness and hospitalization. Few children could fail to be impressed and inquisitive about the mysterious physician-figure, often perceived through distortions of fear, pain, and fever, who was even more powerful than parents.

For those readers who are curious or who like stories with endings, we will return to the chronicle of the woman with the broken arm. But there is a cautionary note: Like every story from real life, and especially from the world of medicine, this one even in its conclusion raises more issues than it puts to rest, and that is perhaps as it should be.

At about one o'clock in the afternoon on Saturday, a week after the accident, the orthopedic surgeon accompanied by a resident arrived to tell the patient that he had diagnosed a fracture. He inquired carefully about the location of the pain, examined the arm and listened attentively to the patient's report of her activities. Because she had not been instructed otherwise, she had been using the arm, had been able to fasten buttons, tie the strings of her hospital gown and even reach behind her head.

The orthopedist then displayed in its purest form the phenomenon known as "piece-of-meat" medicine: the habit of discussing medical management in the presence of a patient as though he or she were not there. Thoughtfully considering the matter with his resident, the surgeon commented that this case presented him with a dilemma. (Note that piece-of-meat medicine has its own language. The case, not the patient is the unit of discourse.) Considering the patient's age, the amount of trauma and surgery she had already undergone, and the fact that some mobility of the arm remained, there could be some argument for allowing healing to continue without further treatment. One disadvantage of this was the possibility that full movement of the arm might be lost. On the other hand, the operative procedure of choice was a major one, would necessitate rather elaborate manipulation of the bones of the arm, and another general anesthetic. If all went well, the patient would probably retain full use of the hand and arm, but there would almost certainly be a marked deformity of the arm. To retain full mobility the patient would have to engage faithfully in a rigorous exercise program beginning postoperatively and continuing for several months. The surgeon was aware that during this same time the woman would have other things to contend with. In addition to the general recovery from both operations, her jaw would remain wired for about seven weeks; liquids would constitute her total diet. She would be incapacitated, might well feel weak and depressed and thus unenthusiastic about exercising. It was indeed a dilemma.

At this point the patient intruded herself, convinced at last that she had a right to have some say in the management of her illness and that the physicians in charge would not voluntarily consult her. She told the surgeon politely but with real feeling how important the use of the right arm was to her, enjoying as she did much handwork and cooking. She was quite willing to chance another operation, would follow to the letter any program of activity which he might prescribe, and live with a deformity of the arm if there was a better chance of ending up with full mobility. The surgeon's response made it clear that a moral judgment of the patient as well as a medical judgment of the situation entered into his final decision. Said he, "Well, with a spirit like that I really think that we should go ahead." And, in fact, he did.

The surgery was a success, and the patient was faithful to her promise, always performing more exercises than the doctor suggested. Healing was uneventful and some ten years later the patient retained full use of the arm and fingers with, as had been predicted, a marked deformity which seemed to trouble her not at all.

This story aroused our interest because it epitomizes so much of what is amiss in health care today. As we examined it, held it to the light and under the magnifying glass, we began to formulate answers to our original perplexity, "How can such a thing happen?" The answers came in several stages, each unfolding onto greater complexity as we came closer to satisfactory solutions. We were convinced that the behavior of physicians and other health-care professionals originates in their training and pre-training experiences. It seemed plain that doctors develop as they are educated and that such development must have order. We thought of this development as a tangled web of developmental lines among which we could distinguish five that seemed to have sufficient explanatory power. But our lines of development were in many ways like growth curves. They were lines of best fit, a smooth approximation of the jagged lines which would summarize the course of many single individuals. If the lines of development were to be hypotheses, not simply a proposal of answers to questions, they needed to be explicit, capable of confirmation or refutation, and they needed to depict the extent of jaggedness as well as the curve of best fit. Matters became even more complicated as the search for precision continued. What had seemed at first to permit representation as lines, or groups of lines, turned out to be planes and eventually three dimensional spaces. And even so the result was not right. The lines-spaces-dimensions were not discreet; they merged and there was order in the combining.

Since we were out of real dimensions and resolved, if possible, to avoid mathematicization, an approximate combination in three dimensions had to be worked out. The specifications for this approximation were clear: The whole had to picture or at least suggest the complexity required for accuracy. To encourage use it also had to be arranged so that, intersected at any point in time it would reveal where each line was individually and as part of the whole. After many tries, an awkward but passable result was constructed which met all the tests. Just to be certain of its flaws as well as its aptness, a physical replica was built. If such literality seems excessive, recall that our intent was to avoid the fanciful and to produce a set of concepts which could be readily understood and applied. Returning for a look at the representation next morning a natural metaphor was inescapable.

"It looks like the roots of a tree!"

"Why the surprise? Isn't that what we have been about—describing the roots from which doctors grow?" And this is how the title, and the book, came into being. After presenting some preliminary definitions and assumptions, we will discuss separately each of the five lines of development. In the final chapter we combine the lines and suggest some ways in which this amalgam can be used.

CHAPTER 2

The Roots of the Tree

For any who doubt that medicine still arouses people's curiosity, a glance at the television programs listed in any daily newspaper will be convincing. Individual "doctor shows" come and go, but the category is a staple, at least as dependable a drawing card as sports events, soap operas, and situation comedies. Scientists have not escaped the lure. There are many thoughtful, written descriptions of how people come to follow medicine as a career, the processes of training which enable them to do the work, and the nature of the whole edifice of medicine which can be thought of as a cult, a subculture, a societal substructure, or all three and more. In another account, (R. N. Zabarenko et al. 1970) we have reviewed papers from 1926 (Simmel) to 1970 concerned with the psychological roots, the psychodynamics of physicians. And O'Malley (1970) has provided an encyclopedic yet readable account of the history of medical education. But the necessary framework for housing and unifying knowledge in these areas is nowhere to be found. It was no less a challenge than the quest for such a construction which led to this work.

Glossary

The language used in describing our hypotheses includes terms from different fields: colloquial English, medicine, vocational and developmental psychology, and psychoanalytic theory. Many cross-disciplinary efforts come to grief because they are studded with terms that are encumbered as well as enriched with many meanings. When these are not defined explicitly or their meanings remain unrestricted, the reader is unnecessarily burdened by having to guess which of the meanings is being implied. The definitions listed below are intended as a move toward clarity, not an attempt at ultimate validity. If there are differences of opinion about how the words should be defined, this can be fruitful. But no reciprocal discussion can begin without definitions.

Mature operating physician. A physician who has successfully integrated medical knowledge and appropriate personality attributes into a functioning whole. Operationally, he can be observed to enjoy working as a physician and maintains a successful relationship with his practice by providing good care and receiving adequate personal satisfaction.

Physicianhood. The combination of internal psychological support elements essential for the work of the mature physician. Physicianhood may include varying levels of intellectual achievement and a large variety of personality structures.

Intensity of relatedness to practice. The degree to which medical practice and healing functions are perceived as psychologically sustenant. At its most intense, this is evidenced in a strong devotion to the practice and can be encompassed and explained by a number of factors. These factors will constitute the outcomes of the lines of development to be discussed below and include: nurturant tendencies, easy activation of care-giving, a strongly held ideal of medical identity, the capacity for rapid shifts between objectivity and empathy within the clinical process, and a species of intrusive curiosity about the human body and its contents. The objection may be raised that relatedness to the practice has its roots in less lofty motives, especially fiscal ones. As the satirist Tom Lehrer puts it, many decide "to specialize in diseases of the rich." Certainly, doctors are not immune to needs for financial security or the pleasures and comforts of affluence. In fact, one often hears cynical comments from physicians themselves about how lucrative the calling is. But the usual rationalizations about high fees to make up for long training and its high costs do not quite settle these issues. Why do doctors acquiesce in jokes about their prosperity? We venture the guess, based on observation, that they feel some shame about the intensity of their devotion to their calling and hide the embarrassment over this seeming sentimentality by appearing to concur in society's misjudgment. The intensity of relatedness to practice cannot satisfactorily be explained by material greed alone, for there are better and quicker routes to achieve that. The psychological aspects must be the key, and we shall be trying to say how as we proceed.

Early symbiosis.[1]   This term has been borrowed from the developmental studies of Margaret Mahler (1968) and her students. Essentially an umbrella word used as an abbreviation to describe several decades of carefully documented work by Mahler and other child psychologists and researchers, it refers to phenomena that have been observed repeatedly in hundreds of settings and are widely accepted among analysts and even nonanalytic professionals as a useful framework for thinking about the interactions between mother and child. In the first two to three years after birth, the infant is biologically dependent upon the mother or other nurturant figures. The newborn is assumed to be incapable of differentiating between himself and his mother, that is, he has a functional concept about himself and his world which is utterly egocentric. (A technical phrase from psychoanalysis often applied to this state is *primary narcissism.*) In subsequent development, work begins toward the discontinuation of the dependence and eventual autonomy. Important structures of personality result from the events of this period. There are visible, behavioral signs of the work which goes on as the infant progresses from a concept of himself as not separate from the mother through a number of stages to a concept of himself as distinct and independent. The links between the internal events and the behavioral manifestations of them can be seen most readily in young

---

1. It is important to say that we have not only borrowed Mahler's term, but simplified it. An exact delineation of the correct technical use of the terminology that has resulted from her discoveries and those of her students can be found in the references. We have used *early symbiosis* here as a suggestive analogy rather than in its precise meaning.

children. There is substantial evidence that residual effects of this maturational process have a pervasive effect upon human personality. We shall be attempting to demonstrate that these residues and the varying routes by which the maturation was accomplished can be seen in physicians in the manner in which they are related to their practices and in some physicians to their patients.

Paracognitive.   This term is a new one, so far as we can tell, and will need some background information as a springboard for definition. One may think about medical education using models similar to those which have been useful in conceptualizing the physics of the atom. A sample is presented in figure 1. The internal sphere labeled A represents an amount of knowledge, a critical mass of information, indispensable for doing the work. In some medical settings this is called the *data base,* and is pegged at different levels according to the expectations teachers have for learners at each stage. The orbits labeled B are built upon this foundation of data and represent the acquisition of various clinical skills—perceptual, psychomotor, psychological, and so on.

For example, one may know the anatomy of the genitourinary system well; this would be somewhere within the area marked A. However, the insertion of a catheter into the urinary bladder is a clinical skill combining the ability to integrate perceptions of the visible anatomy with constructs about the unobservable anatomy, dexterity sufficient to make the procedure minimally uncomfortable and as rapid as possible, and a continuous and sensitive awareness of the patient's feelings.

FIGURE 1

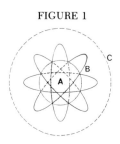

As a second example consider the treatment of pneumonia in a three-year-old child. This would require that the doctor have data about normal development quickly available to recall, that he be capable of distinguishing normal and abnormal chest sounds, and that he pay attention to the toxic state of the sick child and the apprehension of the parents. He would also need to know the kinds of antibiotics likely to be effective for the variety of pneumonia diagnosed, the formulae for calculating the dosage appropriate for the child, the importance of support procedures such as bed rest, liquids, and diet, and how to prescribe medication for symptomatic relief, such as expectorants or pain relievers. As in the first example, clinical skills include accurate perception of the patient and the disease processes, psychomotor deftness which permits a thorough but well-focused physical examination, and sensitivity to the psychological status of the family unit. These skills are built upon and combined with knowledge from scientific fields such as pharmacology, infectious diseases, and the pathophysiology of the respiratory system.

The space designated as C in figure 1 is that part of the student's mind which incorporates and supports both the acquisition of knowledge—the continuous gathering and sharpening of skills—and the integration of these as a component of the personality of the physician-to-be. This region is what we have called the *paracognitive,* a word evoked by dissatisfaction with terms now in use. It has become eminently clear that more than good cognitive functioning is required to produce a mature operating physician. The problem has been to isolate and describe the vital additional features. In some cases all of the features of adequate medical performance which are not intellective have been designated *noncognitive.* For us this term represents the same kind of potential risk as diagnosis by exclusion. For example, are the kinds of skills just described (those employed in urinary catheterization and treating pneumonia) cognitive or noncognitive? Most medical school faculty would readily agree that depending upon the specific skill and the zone of the body in which it is deployed, both kinds of factors are involved in learning.

The term *affective* has also been used to describe the nonintellectual aspects of physician performance. Technically, *affective* means related or pertaining to the emotions, and this seems too diffuse. For most medical educators it is precisely the appropriate balance of objectivity and the capacity for feeling with the patient which characterizes the best physicians. Lists of attributes, habits, and attitudes are usually too particulate. They fail to capture the interrelationship between what has been taught conventionally and overtly as necessary for doctoring and those patterns of thought and behavior often learned unknowingly which are also truly essential for the work.

We define as paracognitive those aspects of psychological functioning which support and encourage learning processes—the acquisition of adequate amounts of knowledge, and the development and perfection of sufficient skills—and unify them into a cohesive, professional whole. These features of the personality are crucial for learning and determine its direction, style, and intensity. Paracognitive factors constitute the background, substrate, and limits for medical education and maturation.

If these elements, encompassed by circle C in figure 1, have been poorly comprehended, there can be at least two reasons. They are difficult to observe and measure and, like most intangibles of this sort, easier to discount or ignore than grapple with. Secondly, in most learners where paracognitive supports are adequate, they need no attention. It is when the structures are imperfect or worse, defective, and education falters or stops, that their existence and importance become clearest.

Residues of the oedipal resolutions in physicians. This phrase relies for its meaning on an understanding of what constitutes an effective resolution of the oedipal conflict or the oedipal complex in a general sense. The following description is abstracted from *A Glossary of Psychoanalytic Terms and Concepts* (Moore et al. 1968), a pamphlet prepared "by organized psychoanalysis to clarify in simple, understandable language what is meant by its terms and concepts."

The oedipus complex is a characteristic grouping of drives, aims, relationships with significant persons (technically called object relations), and fears found during the ages of three to six years. The complex "is a nodal point crucial to the further growth and development of the immature psychic apparatus; through its resolution it contributes to the coalescence and definitive formulation of the superego" (p. 66), the latter being "a theoretical concept designating those psychic functions which in their manifest expression represent moral attitudes, conscience and a sense of guilt" (p. 90). "The complex is usually partly conscious and evident in speech, behavior and other modes of communication during childhood. In later life it is most often unconscious but dependent upon the extent of resolution, is more or less evident in behavior, attitudes and object choice [the conscious choice of a loved person] and has an important bearing on character structure, the nature of object relationships and sexual identity, fantasy formation and later sexual patterns and activities" (p. 66). *Oedipal conflict* is a term which refers to characteristic conflicts arising from the oedipus complex including "active and passive aims . . . , masculine and feminine identifications" (p. 67).

There remain in everyone aspects of the personality in which the resolution of the oedipus complex and its accompanying conflicts are incomplete. Such residues are not necessarily pathologic or pathogenic; they contribute to the uniqueness of each personality. Elements of the residuals of this conflict can be observed, along with those from preceding and succeeding periods of development, in anxiety about rivalries, relationships with authority figures, and fear of failure. These problems and the way they are solved have special importance for and lend a special cast to development in doctors.

In observing medical students, we have noticed preservation and enhancement from the oedipal period (and earlier) of identifications with nurturant and active mastering parent figures. During the oedipal period the child copes with a triangular situation, his attachments to parents of the same and opposite sex. It involves perception of and confrontation with gender differences and the setting up of differential patterns of interaction with males and females. Prior to this developmental period, sexual role-distinctions have not been important. It is also significant that sterotypes linking nurturance to females and active mastering behavior to males often occur in the mind of the child, which is, to be sure, strongly influenced by cultural forces. But these are not necessarily valid distinctions for adults. Each child can have highly varying experiences concerning the perception of gender-linked stereotypes.

Understanding of the psychological significance of the physician's authority role, the heavy masculinization of the profession, and the importance of nurturance in its performance will be furthered by recalling the experiences of the oedipal phase and its residues.

Organizing trauma.   This idea, advanced recently by child psychoanalysts, is based on evidence derived from normal development rather than from psychopathology. The term refers to the events which occur when a traumatic experience impinging from outside the person has an impact extensive enough to require revision of psychological functioning (Kestenberg 1961). Depending upon the developmental stage and the sturdiness of the personality, such traumata may be destructive or even catastrophic, especially if they occur too early. But they can also be beneficial and promote growth if timing is developmentally fortunate. For example, the experience of seeing violent behavior, especially sexual, may contribute to a fear of or fascination with such situations in the adult. Under different circumstances or in a different youngster such events, though upsetting, may stimulate mastery of the anxiety as well as of some portion of the environment. One technique of mastery appears in some adolescents and adults as a kind of persistent and intrusive curiosity which gives an edge and enthusiasm to learning—and if the curiosity comes to be focused on the human body it is especially helpful for medical training.

Focus on the body.   In those with a well-developed sense of physicianhood, many aspects of the human body have a special importance. This can be observed in the way a doctor senses, perceives, and manipulates the patient. Touching is part of clinical exploration, and curiosity about the inner workings of the body supports the kind of professional investigation which is essential for good medical care. The point can be made, of course, that the physician's special focus on the body is no more significant than the artist's fascination with his medium, the mechanic's curiosity about machinery, or the lawyer's preoccupation with right, wrong, and rules. The response seems plainly that the arena of work must be an important determinant of vocational choice. The doctor's "choice" of the body as something intriguing, whether that choice was conscious or not, remains a point relevant to this calling and to our study.

But no aspect of this study is as simple as the last sentence implies. Physicians are preoccupied with the human body in a special way. Their interest extends to the total entity. It includes those aspects which can be known only by means of sensory extenders like the fluoroscope and x-ray, and encompasses processes which go on in arenas so small that they can be seen only through the microscope, or so complex that they must be inferred from biochemical assays. The focus we speak of refers not only to the zeroing-in of attention, but to the intense and unceasing interest that doctors display, especially in their need to know as much as possible and at every level available to them.

Physician ego-ideal. The concept of the ego-ideal is one of Freud's later constructs. Since its precise use is not universally agreed upon by psychoanalysts (although most acknowledge its usefulness) the generic definition that appears in the glossary makes the best starting point. The ego-ideal is defined as "the image of the self to which the individual aspires both consciously and unconsciously, and against which he measures himself. It is based on identification with parents and other early environmental figures as they actually are, were in the past or as they have been idealized. To the extent that the actual self does not measure up to the ego-ideal, the person's self-esteem suffers" (p. 43).

For the physician, the ego-ideal constitutes his expectations of himself as a doctor. His internalized standards allow him automatically to sift and process information about the level of his work and feel swiftly signals of deficiences in performance. When such signals are activated, they are usually accompanied by feelings of shame; the doctor may or may not be fully aware of or able to understand his distress.

As one example, consider the behavior of the orthopedic surgeon in the case of the woman with the broken arm. For those who knew this physician well, his behavior that Saturday morning was surprising, very different from his customary sensitivity to patients' feelings. What made him regress to piece-of-meat medicine? Only guesses are possible, but one explanation might be as follows. If his embarrassment was unconscious, that is, if he was uncomfortable but not fully aware of the components of shame in his discomfort, it may have been because this patient had been neglected by colleagues with whom he felt a kind of kinship and within an institution to which he felt some loyalty. The facts must have been for him a clear signal that his colleagues and the institution had fallen far short of the standards of his physician ego-ideal. Under the stress of the moment (like any other human being) he responded with atypical behavior, certainly not truly representative of his best self. The regression surfaced in a moralistic judgment ("she is really a good patient") which led to excellent medical care at last. Moreover, in the months and years after the surgery during which routine checks necessitated frequent contact with the surgeon, the woman became one of his pets, a person he liked and admired and who was accorded many special privileges by him and his staff. Suffice it to say that expiation of guilt or relief from shame from any source, rational or irrational, can take many forms.

In defining the ego-ideal, it is important to differentiate between the doctor's expectations for himself and his idealism about medicine. The former is a psychological entity he can arrange to live with, a personal set of performance standards; the latter is often what he feels he must espouse and teach, a form of professional conscience. The importance of this distinction is especially relevant to medical education. Any discussion involving standards, which are, in this context, a reflection of each doctor's notions about what medicine ought to be, is apt to elicit strong feelings. For the student there may be a puzzling contradiction. It is as though some early experiences with parenting figures were being repeated and teachers were saying, "Do as I say, not as I do (or have done)." It is as hard for outsiders or neophytes to understand the underlying conviction in this apparent duplicity as it is for the child to comprehend his parents' motivation. Confused and baffled, many content themselves with epithets; they choose to believe that teachers are hypocritical, envious, or simply inept, or that they hold each generation to increasingly higher standards in order to gain some revenge for the indignities of their own student days. The fact is that most faculty knowingly urge students to achievements which are beyond what they, the teachers, will ever reach. But they do this in part out of a belief that the quality of medical professionals must always improve, because this is the most direct way in which ever better medical care can be ensured.

We will need one further extension of the generic definition of the ego-ideal. Just as the ego-ideal of each person is shaped by identifications with early figures or fantasies about how they were or should have been, the physician ego-ideal is often modeled upon the real or imagined characteristics of other physicians, including those encountered in childhood and in the course of training.

Objectivity-empathy continuum. The objectivity that constitutes one end of this continuum is an affect state characterized by cool evenhandedness in the gathering and weighing of information as part of adequate investigation. Empathy, the other pole, is a state in which transient yet forceful identifications with the feelings of the patient are used to obtain data.

Many physicians and educators believe empathy to be an affect that may serve as a motivator but can also be a distraction. This viewpoint fails to take into account the information-gathering potential in empathy. This potential is particularly vital for physicians. Unless they can, through trial identifications, gain some appreciation of where the patient is vis-à-vis his illness, the doctor, and the treatment, pieces of information crucial to adequate comprehension may very well be missed. For the terminal patient, the noncompliant patient, and the chronically ill patient without hope of cure, the inability of the physician to empathize may result in increased suffering or even a threat to life and cause the doctor's valid dissatisfaction with himself and the therapeutic result.

It is perhaps unnecessary to belabor the need for objectivity in learning to become a doctor or in practicing as one. But it is essential to recognize that failures in patient care can also occur when the objectivity end of the continuum is hypertrophied. Objectivity and empathy support learning in different ways. From the interaction of his own developmental history and his training, the physician should experience growth throughout the range of the continuum, and the breadth, flexibility, mobility, and speed of oscillation in this area should increase and deepen.

Numerous efforts have been made to study this process without clear success, and perhaps this is because of the evanescent, highly mobile qualities of the internal processes involved. These are difficult to capture in questionnaires, discussions, or inventories. They are available more readily, but never easily, to techniques such as introspection and close observation of doctor-patient transactions.

Nurturant tendencies.   These are defined as the readiness to assume a relation with others similar to that which parents typically have to a child. In early years this relationship includes not only caretaking but protection. In the developing physician as in all adults, these tendencies will have been heavily influenced by the way in which he or she was cared for or wished to be cared for. To be sure, these archaic feelings are modulated in the doctor-adult by realistic considerations of self-preservation and cultural and professional appropriateness. But the most important fact is that in physicianhood they can be expressed in uniquely fitting and gratifying ways—in work which accurately fits the patients' and doctors' needs and thus results in mutual gratification.

Activation of healing behavior.   This we define as a readiness to respond to varying degrees and kinds of helplessness (nurturant need) with behavior which is adequate and appropriate. In the physician these responses become professionalized as the result of learning and maturation. In time they can become so rapid that even a practiced observer is dazzled, left with the question, "How in the world did he do that?"

The mature operating physician has a repertoire of modes which determine how healing behavior will be implemented. Much of the repertoire he holds in common with other colleagues who do similar work, but some maneuvers are utterly his own. They become the core of his style. (L. M. Zabarenko et al. 1968; R. N. Zabarenko et al. 1970). As an example of commonly held variations in the speed and urgency of activation of healing impulses, consider first a patient in cardiac arrest. This situation will mobilize almost instantly in virtually all doctors (and many others) healing efforts at an impressive level of intensity. The report of one observer is illustrative. He was watching as a group of four physicians, three nurses, and three unidentified technical assistants tried to resuscitate an elderly woman in cardiac arrest in an intensive care unit. The odor of human perspiration in the room was almost overpowering. Obviously it was not the patient who was sweating.

At the other end of the continuum is the patient, familiar to any physician, who is a regular weekly or biweekly visitor to the office. His complaints are vague but persistent, and often he has been evaluated by specialists and clinics with findings which do not yield a diagnosis enabling the doctor to work, but only confirming the absence of serious or life-threatening disease. Sometimes the sight of such a patient's name on the schedule can deactivate most of the doctor's desire to heal, because the need for healing *seems* absent and previous attempts have been so discouraging for both doctor and patient.

Any physician, or anyone who has ever been a patient, will be able to fill in points along the continuum between the two extremes of activation, i.e., cardiac arrest and poorly defined illness situations. As concrete evidence of the powerful effect of each physician's individual style, there is the mutual selection which results in time in a practice which unites a physician and patient group who are compatible. As every doctor knows, there are always the doctor-shoppers and floaters, but the stability of any practice represents, at a psychological level, a fit between the doctor's system of activating the healing urge and the patients' needs.

This term and the preceding one both refer to psychological

phenomena with internal correlates which are essentially behavioral and thus observable. Perhaps because of this, they have been well studied (Balint 1964; Clyne 1963) and are more easily understood than some of the other items in the glossary. Our goal will be to show the connections between such recognizable processes and some of the hypothetical internal phenomena we propose which are not quite so visible.

Assumptions

The assumptions that form the substructure of our work fall into three domains in a descending order of conceptual and empirical inclusiveness. Some are sufficiently broad to apply to most of behavioral science, others are germane to human development, others are mainly relevant to medical education.

Like sociologists, psychologists, anthropologists, psychiatrists, and some historians, we believe that human behavior is lawful and knowable, even though the sector of nature we work with is complicated, and at present draws upon a small store of established fact when compared with its sister sciences. But the conviction remains that methodical investigation based on the same scientific principles that have yielded such impressive results in physics, chemistry, and biology will lead eventually to comparable advances in appreciating the complexities of the human condition and, in time, to improving it.

In the realm of developmental psychology we share with many others the assumption that the outcome of early maturational processes significantly affects those which follow. It is not simply that early events are important. There are two corollaries: (1) Later development is superimposed upon the strengths and vulnerabilities of preceding stages. (2) Given the marvelous adaptive potential of humans, the vicissitudes of early growth cannot completely determine what is to follow; they can, however, and we believe they do, influence development in specific and highly individual ways.

As must already be suspected, we believe that a number of discoveries from psychoanalysis are valid and that they are capable of useful transposition to developmental psychology. Many aspects of psychoanalytic thought have already been absorbed into general and developmental psychology and psychiatry. Frequently this incorporation has not been accompanied by an acknowledgment of the source; and in addition, the acceptance of psychoanalytic concepts is selective, often selective enough to amount to distortion. For this reason we have defined above in the glossary our precise use of psychoanalytic terms.

The third assumption relevant to developmental psychology pertains to the issue of critical phases. And it is an issue. A recent advanced textbook in developmental psychology (Endler, Boulter and Osser 1968) contains five chapters devoted to extensive reviews of the literature, firm positions pro (Scott) and con (Denenberg, Caldwell), and a variety of experimental evidence including affectional systems in monkeys (Harlow) and imprinting in birds (Hess). Informed of the points to be made on both sides of this question we remain convinced of the usefulness of two aspects of the critical stage hypothesis: There are periods of maximum susceptibility to certain classes of stimuli, and the same stimulus has different effects upon an organism at different ages. There may be limited time intervals in development during which certain classes of stimuli are effective in producing profound behavioral effects, but beyond this critical time period these same stimuli may have little or no effect.

Working with the definitions and assumptions already given, we can formulate a statement regarding the problem at hand, the education of physicians. We believe that medical education can best be understood not as training, but as a lawful developmental process—one which can be monitored and charted, encompasses critical periods, and is influenced crucially by events occurring early in the life of the student and early in his or her training. This is really the leitmotif of all that will follow. Previous efforts to explain how doctors are made were unproductive because events were viewed only as an educational process. When considered developmentally, room becomes available to house the complexities we know to be valid, but which had had to be amputated to fit simplistic frames.

In medical education as in all development, individual students will vary in the rate at which they progress. We can predict that these rates will be influenced by psychological, educational, temporal, and cultural factors and perhaps many more. We may also assume that for those students whose progress is outside the usual ranges, either too fast or too slow, special attention will be required. And this brings us to our last two major assumptions.

There are many ways in which developmental processes can be conceptually accommodated. The most congenial and useful for us was the idea that successive stages of development overlap; they interface and build upon one another. This is not an original idea. It has served well such distinguished students of human development as Piaget (1954), S. Freud (1905), A. Freud (1965), Erikson (1950), Spitz and Cobliner, and many others. The emphasis on expected variability in learning and development, on a multidimensional concept of growth with interlocking, multilayered processes offered just the kind of intellectual maneuvering room we needed.

The last assumption is the most theoretical and tenuous of all. To be perfectly candid about the chronological order of things, it is more a conviction resulting from the work than an assumption with which we began. At advanced levels of development, processes escalate, and permutations occur; quantum leaps or surges are characteristic. To illustrate this assumption we offer two examples of less complex kinds of learning. It is known that there is an optimum age—a critical time or stage—during which children can best learn to play the piano. For most children this occurs around the seventh or eight year. The first stages include learning to read music, to see a cylindrical shape on a grid of lines and recognize it as D. Then this perception must be correlated with the depression of a key on the piano. Though students vary in the length of time and the difficulty with which they accomplish this part of the total task, a large majority succeed. The next stage involves putting the notes together in various arrangements of gradually increasing difficulty; many students learn enough to be able to play some major works in the piano repertoire—Beethoven sonatas, Mozart concerti, large suites such as the Saint-Saëns *Carnaval* or the Chopin impromptus. Note that thus far most of our developmental assumptions have been illustrated. Each step in the learning builds upon and is interrelated with what has gone before. But at this point the process takes an unusual surge. It is one kind of accomplishment to play Debussy, but to understand fully the musical significance of a work such as the Rachmaninoff Third Piano Concerto and to be able to perform with a symphony orchestra in such a manner as to make this understanding clear to an audience represents an achievement of another order of magnitude.

As another example, consider golf. The earliest stages involve learning to coordinate matters so that the contact between the club and the ball occurs as regularly as possible. Progressively other tasks are undertaken: lengthening the drive, precision in the "short game," and accuracy in putting. Still later the dilemmas of how to get out of sand traps, how to avoid water, rough, and forests may be solved. As these stages build upon one another and practice continues, the result may be a good golfer whose skills are reflected in a low handicap. But there comes a point at which cumulated skills coalesce. There is a great difference between the good golfer's approach to the game and that of the professional. The pro wants to place his drive so he can reach the green with his second shot. His calculations will include information about the wind speed and direction, his knowledge of the terrain of each hole, especially its hazards, and the psychological state of his opponents. To succeed he must, like the musician, harness cognition and emotional discipline. Neither will panic at a lost hole or wrong note. The tasks of earlier stages of learning, long since mastered, will have receded but not disappeared from consideration.

One possible explanation for the quantum leap from mastery to integration and synthesis is that when certain physical skills become automatic, and when mature understanding is fully internalized, a critical mass is reached which produces the professional—the musician or the athlete. It can be no accident that the number of learners capable of making this kind of advance is significantly smaller than those who develop up to that point.

Something similar occurs in the development of physicians. The last stages of development begin later, progress more slowly, reach or near completion in fewer individuals, and have much greater ranges within which individuals can still do the work, i.e., practice medicine. It is as though the most advanced stages were supra-developmental events.

The Roots of the Tree

In the chapters that follow we shall describe five lines of development in the maturation toward physicianhood. Each has observable manifestations and displays variability in onset, length, intensity, and completeness of mastery. All are overlapping, so that achievement in later stages is heavily contingent upon that in earlier ones and upon the period in which early achievement occurred. The first three lines represent the kind of developmental progress seen in the early stages of many kinds of complex learning. The last two, slower to begin, slower to mature, more rarely approaching the highest levels, seem of a supraordinate variety. Like the others, they build upon previous stages and involve the necessity for synthesizing previous learning and experience. But they involve the quantum leap. In a crude way, it is like the contrast between arithmetic and geometric progressions.

The five stages are listed here as tasks because one good way to think about physicians' development is the manner in which these problems are solved:

1. Balancing the oscillation between objectivity and empathy
2. Appropriate management of nurturant tendencies and executive necessities
3. Adequate regulation and control of needs for omnipotence by appropriate appreciation of the realities of medical work, especially those related to the tolerance for uncertainty
4. Formation of an internal ideal of physicianhood—a professional ego-ideal
5. Maturation of an operational professional identity.

In their final or maximal form of development these five lines can serve as a job description for the end product, a physician, specified in internal terms and in a statement of how the internal state was achieved and how it works.

The roster of tasks can also be thought of as paracognitive factors in learning. We will present evidence at many points to support our conviction that sufficient mastery of paracognitive factors must coincide with or precede cognitive mastery; together these two currents constitute adequate development. In medicine particularly, paracognitive factors must be adequate to support an enormous cognitive enterprise. Furthermore, no account of medical education which fails to consider paracognitive factors can claim either a sufficient degree of completeness or the likelihood of predictive power.

Material will be presented in a number of categories for each line of development. Precursors, those events occurring before medical education begins, will be of special importance. Much of the data in this category will draw on research in general human development and on reconstructions from the treatment of adult patients. The links between this kind of information and the schema of lines will be suggestive, designed to be evocative and to generate hypotheses.

Concrete examples and observable manifestations of the events in each developmental line will also be presented. But as some of the lines have very long growth periods, we can only sample the data along the way. In addition to events which occur during medical studies, we will examine data relevant to three pivotal events which occur before medical school and have the advantage of being recognizable and definable. Certainly any maturational process has many turning points. These three were chosen because they have repeatedly loomed as crucial in our experiences with medical students and practicing physicians.

The first turning point is the initial internal recognition of the wish to become a physician. Some medical school applicants can recall not only the time but the events that led them toward medicine. For others, remembering the circumstances of this internal event is difficult, suggesting that it may be the object of repression or obscured by developmental overlays. In the psychoanalytic treatment of physicians, the causes and time of the earliest turn toward physicianhood can sometimes be recovered (see Glauber 1953). The apparent amnesia may have many determinants, and this situation seems to crop up frequently where one parent is a physician. Many doctors, medical students, and medical school applicants can never remember *not* wanting to be doctors.

The second important event is more easily observed: the first public statement of the intention to become a physician. It must be signficant, although at present we cannot say exactly in what way, how closely the first internal decision to become a doctor and the first public statement of the intent coincide with one another and with general development in the individual. Such data might be relevant when considering candidates for admission.

The third point is the formal commitment to a medical career. Such commitments range along a continuum extending from those who identify themselves as premed in high school through those who decide to apply to a medical school at the end of four years of undergraduate study or even later, after postgraduate work or some other career choice. As a convenient, if arbitrary designation point for this range, we shall assume application to medical school as evidence of strong commitment to the profession.

Another category of data to be described will be the approximate critical stage for each development line. The approximation will suggest the time when learning along the line first begins to pick up speed and also the culminating edge, that point where learning has coalesced into smooth functioning supported by firmly ensconced, paracognitive, psychological structures. It might just as well be said here that the first signs of development and learning are more readily observed than the final coalescence, a state where progress has to be estimated using inferential evidence. For each line the completeness and styles of mastery vary enormously, and we shall try to do justice to this variety. Most emphatically we do not mean to imply that the end of a critical phase means the end of development. What is important for this schema is that the ebbing of developmental surge in one line is usually the signal that acceleration may be about to occur in a succeeding one.

The interwoven, integrated, and yet separately characteristic

FIGURE 2

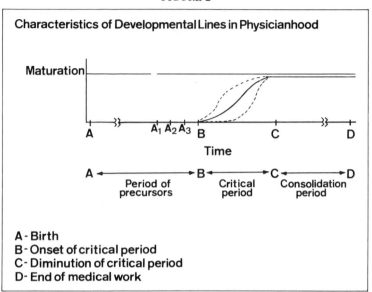

Characteristics of Developmental Lines in Physicianhood

A - Birth
B - Onset of critical period
C - Diminution of critical period
D - End of medical work

ways in which affective states support cognitive mastery and manipulation will be also a focus. Put simply, for each of the paracognitive lines of development the specifics of the way in which this development is related to cognitive mastery will be sampled.

Figure 2 diagrams some of the events just described. The period from birth to the onset of the critical period in a developmental line (points A through B) includes the usual developmental phases of childhood and the three events described earlier as pivotal points, the first private consideration of medicine as a life work, the first public acknowledgement of the fact, and the commitment to the training, application to medical school. The period of maximum development (points B through C) is shown by a curve indicating the kind of increase in development which can occur. The solid line in the curves for each developmental phase will indicate a sort of average or mean; the dotted lines will stand for the dispersion around this mean which includes the expectable and educationally feasible. The consolidation period (C through D on the diagram) represents the coalescence and establishment within the learner of both paracognitive and cognitive achievements.

CHAPTER 3

Developmental Line 1: Managing the Oscillation Between Objectivity and Empathy

There is substantial agreement among many researchers that an individual's capacity to appraise external reality and still remain sensitive to his own inner states has its roots in very early periods of development. The different styles and results of this maturation have been the object of intense study recently by psychologists and psychoanalysts (A. Freud 1958, 1965; Kernberg 1974; Kohut 1971; Mahler 1968). This work has importance for our discussion in many ways. These events are the precursors which determine the intensity and time at which the child's attention is focused on the body and its functions. In the earliest phases of infancy the sense of reality, cognition (or the precursors of it), and life support are fused. So far as is known, the infant is aware only that a nurturant figure, usually the mother, is either present or absent. Later, a distinction evolves between the infant's inner concept of himself and his concept of his mother as a separate entity. One of the results of this is curiosity about the mother's body. With mobility comes generalized curiosity about the body and particularly the genitalia, implemented in preschool years by playing the doctor game (Simmel 1926), by self-observation, and observing parents and siblings.

These events form a developmental sequence so familiar that many parents can observe it. First there is only a sense of being merged with the mother, then recognition of her as a separate being, curiosity about her and other separate nonselves, a deepening of the child's sense of self and autonomy, and much later, beginnings of the ability to feel what others are feeling, that is, to empathize. Although these very early experiences are modified by the events of latency and adolescence, they largely determine the extent to which the special targets of our study, medical students and physicians, can develop both objectivity and empathy. They also determine whether the shuttle between objectivity and empathy will take place with ease, minimal anxiety, and little danger to internal arrangements (psychic homeostasis), or whether it will be constricted, painful, and uneven.

We have been able to discover little documented evidence about how objectivity and empathy are managed prior to medical school. When the first internal and public recognitions of the appeal of medicine occur early or are related to some early childhood figure, such as the family physician, this seems to be a strong, stable motivational current. When the decision for medicine is made later in life and via educational or vocational detours, the major motivating forces may be as strong but lack the effects of an early crystallizing focus. It seems reasonable to conjecture that when young people are dubious or hesitant about medicine, one part of their reluctance may be traced to the question of whether the primary mode of interpersonal work will be most comfortably anchored to objectivity or empathy. The idea of alternation between these two is a new one and rests upon training as well as predisposition.

Styles of learning during premedical studies are measurably different; they are assumed to be relevant and crucial predictors of success in medical school. According to the 1974 summary of score distributions for the Medical College Admissions Test (1975, p. 2): "Examinees indicating a major in the humanities (including languages and the arts) earn considerably higher scores in verbal ability in the general information (subtest) than those from any other field. Correspondingly, majors in physical sciences (including chemistry and mathematics) excelled on the quantitative ability and science sections of the MCAT. This pattern . . . has occurred annually." These data underscore the fact that the either-or attitude toward objectivity and empathy as cognitive and paracognitive styles is reflected in the majors and grades of undergraduate medical students, and these in turn are largely determined by known selection criteria.

One corrective measure for the problems involved in selecting and preparing applicants for medical school might be to introduce as early as possible the idea that learning conditions for medicine are optimal when the student has reservoirs of both objectivity and empathy. More than that, one good clue about the students who will in the end make the best doctors may be seen first in the capacity to be flexible. And the ability to alternate between objective and empathic modes may well be reflected in a broad variety of successfully completed and enjoyed premedical courses, as opposed to a narrow focus on quantitative subjects.

Individuals at the outer extremes of the range we propose can be recognized, as can their likelihood of running into difficulty in medical studies. Consider, for example, the undergraduate physical science or mathematics major applying for medical school who is plainly at a loss in maintaining any but the most distant or uncomfortable interpersonal relationships. If this difficulty is a fixed, and not a temporary psychological position, and if the candidate is accepted, it can be predicted that difficulties will arise during the clinical years in relating to patients—in obtaining an adequate history or gaining patient cooperation for difficult procedures. Identification of such extreme cases of poor paracognitive aptitude for medical work is not difficult, but is not always implemented. (The above statements should not be taken as a simple or polemic endorsement of wide-ranging course selection in the liberal arts or humanities for premedical students. It is intrapsychic flexibility which needs to be estimated. That is a complicated entity, and one unlikely to be entirely or completely reflected in course choices or even in grades in these courses.)

As this example illustrates, care must be taken to distinguish the student passing through a development era from one locked into a lifelong position. It is not uncommon for medical students (as for many others) to experience occasional feelings of faintness at the sight of blood, to suffer a spell of anxiety while observing an amputation, or feel revulsion as a draining bed sore is dressed. These disequilibria can often be mastered via the developmental mechanisms we are discussing. But where such affective disruptions persist, the student will be handicapped not only in learning many aspects of basic medical science, but in mustering the general intrusiveness and aggression needed for medical work. For example, performing endoscopy, pelvic examinations, or surgery will be difficult, and although students may prevail against these liabilities, the necessary internal adjustments are likely to be costly. (The important link between this line of development and adequate management of aggression is the first of a number of dynamic strands which will recur across more than one of the lines.)

The premedical student who has the best chance of achieving physicianhood needs more than adequate cognitive skills: He must also have the freedom to move to empathic perceptual modes and responses. These are not necessarily, or even importantly, a verbal matter. The capacity to feel vividly and accurately if only briefly the suffering of another person begins a fortunate circle. If such brief identifications are possible and occur in a person with the capacity for cognitive mastery, they will be forged into an imperative, responsible urge toward healing. This of itself lends strong support to cognitive learning and application, reinforcing and underscoring the entire process. The real challenge, therefore, lies in accurate discrimination within the vast middle range. Although applicants vary greatly, most will fall within educable ranges in their capacities to deal with three component functions of this developmental era: (1) the ability to experience, control, and use empathy; (2) mastery of basic knowledge and skills so that cognitive content information can be rapidly and accurately scanned; and (3) the freedom to use information from both sources to arrive at a unified and coherent perception. Rapid shifts between these functions are necessary and adaptive, but the ability to manage such shifts with increasing speed and comfort will vary.

The critical stage for this line of development seems to begin with basic science instruction in medical school. During this period the student must learn material which, for many, is best mastered in the absence of empathy but in the presence of zest for maturational progress and a realization that the information is necessary. In gross anatomy, for example, empathic identification with the cadaver would certainly impede learning. In mastering the Krebs cycle, the branches of the carotid artery, or the distribution of the cranial nerves, efficient learning may again require not empathy but the steadfast attention of a learner who resists affective distractions. Of course, this very concentration is a manifestation of the paracognitive support system: something within the learner enables him to mobilize the energy to preserve the constancy he needs to achieve mastery.

The faculty who teach the basic medical sciences, the first faculty most medical students encounter, embody the qualities often subsumed under objectivity. Their cognitive style is characterized by careful precision and a steady concentration on content. These teachers (like all others) serve frequently as models—students admire and identify with them, often seek to emulate them. Their approach transmits the message that medical information is best mastered by viewing the human body and its processes as a series of mechanisms. This early learning mode is preserved in the compartments and divisions—so plainly obvious in medical schools, hospitals, and medical life in general—that parallel and reinforce the division of the organism into a series of mechanisms or a group of subsystems or both. Reassembly of the separate pieces into the concept, patient, or further, person, seems to be assumed as something which will occur automatically or at least routinely.

It also seems to be regarded as axiomatic that empathic faculties should be suspended in the early basic science learning, much of which is abstract. There is little real dispute among students or faculty about the fact that the material must be learned. What often creates conflict are two dissonances of life in medical education: (1) The beginning medical student is encouraged to assume a nonempathic set just when the wish to heal is usually experienced strongly, indeed urgently, but is also diffuse, not yet specifically focused. There can be no room for surprise if this unfortunately timed tug-of-war produces problems. (2) In spite of the agreement that the material has to be mastered, conflict may erupt if teachers imply that this knowledge is somehow sufficient in itself rather than necessary as a footer upon which to mount the rest of medical information. The phenomenon that has been called cynicism by Becker et al. (1961) and Rezler (1974) may be, in fact, an outer reflection of the students' struggles with these differing views and their underlying and opposite value systems.

This particular dilemma has been an issue for at least three thousand years (Kudlien 1970). In ancient Greece the classification of medical knowledge was the subject of controversy. In that civilization medicine began and for a time was confined to traumatology and epidemiology. It was practiced mainly in the streets and viewed as a useful and necessary craft. With Hippocrates, Aristotle, and others, physicians began to concern themselves with other areas such as the fluids, structure, and unseen functions of the body. At this point, in accordance with Greek tradition, medicine transcended craft and had to be regarded as a division of knowledge. Since all knowledge must come from the gods, it was assumed that Apollo himself had transmitted the knowledge of medicine to Aesculapius, and he in turn had disseminated it to his followers.

A related fact is that a cadaver has traditionally been the students' "first patient." Lewin (1946) suggested that this custom might help the student to avoid interfering empathic impulses. But even so, there are outcroppings of affect, and these often occur when anatomical studies require procedures which would be impossible in the living human—removing the calvarium, or the progressive study and destruction of the genitalia. We hypothesize that the queasiness, giggling, and gallows humor which students manifest at these times can best be explained by remembering that such instances must evoke sadistic, masochistic, and aggressive feelings. Thus, although the obliging cadaver does not permit the student to bypass his empathic responses completely, it does expose him to a management mode which may become a lifelong template for the doctor-patient relationship. The cadaver cannot be hurt, it has no subtle sensitivities to complicate things, and it cannot speak. In short, everything about it discourages empathic identification. During the study and mastery of gross anatomy, feelings of confidence and justifiable pride often emerge from the student's original curiosity, horror, and titillation.

The cadaver's impassivity can be an important contribution in allowing this kind of development to occur. In the dissecting room one often hears students musing about the lives of the people who have become "their cadavers." Fantasies about how they came to arrive on the dissecting table are frequent. Perhaps at these moments the objective cognition of anatomic study has been interrupted or mildly ruffled by affective currents which could be aggressive and erotic. In any case, reactions to the cadaver-patient, capable of being observed in any medical school, support the notion that modified empathic functions persist even with the dead preparation, although to be sure they have been temporarily shunted from the foreground. Even at this stage there is interest in the person as well as in the body, and the interest is tenacious. It cannot be accidental that what many physicians think of as "good" patients display similarities to the cadaver: they are compliant, don't intrude feeling into the treatment, and are mostly quiet.

Another polarity which can generate conflict in early medical education is perhaps less obvious, but still extremely potent: it is plain fact that in many ways medicine and academic scholarship have opposite values and customs. The issues involved in this ideational collision have been summarized recently by Rose (1974) and could undoubtedly be traced back into the history of medicine mentioned earlier. An important facet of scholarly work is that knowledge is the coin of the realm and its ultimate version is the written, i.e., printed and published, word. This occurs in some fields of medicine too, of course. But much valuable medical knowledge is transmitted orally, even oracularly, which means, among other things, that large portions of knowledge can be restricted to the profession. The charge has been made that in this way physicians preserve the feeling of Aesculapian exclusiveness. While there may be some truth to this, the matter is not so simple.

Intimacy is a prerequisite for the oral sharing of important knowledge. From this we can derive an interesting parallel. For effective healing to take place there must be some kind of intimacy between doctor and patient. The degree and species of this intimacy will vary enormously with the mutual capacities and needs of doctor and patient. But most physicians strive for a therapeutic relationship in which there is no possibility of error resulting from intimacy. That is, they want to ensure treatment that will be effective no matter how the doctor feels about or relates to the patient. Another aspect of the parallelism has to do with the intimacy required (in medicine and in other professions) between teacher and student. The large oral component in medical knowledge can be translated psychologically as follows. It is as though the master physician-teacher said, "My knowledge is power. I will share it with you only if you are close to me." Such feelings become more frequent as the medical student emerges from the intense study of basic sciences and has more contact with clinical teachers. It is our hypothesis that this is the time when the most beneficial and complete learning occurs and also when the developmental stage which is involved with managing the oscillation between objectivity and empathy will begin its maximum surge. This hypothesis assumes that the student will have retained his empathic capacities even though they may have been shelved during the basic science studies. The completeness and styles of mastery for this phase can most often be observed in clinical work as the developmental acceleration begins to taper off, usually in the senior year of medical school. One indication of mastery is the student's ability to receive knowledge in the oral, intimate manner we have been describing.

Often the treasured wisdom imparted in this mode is not particularly profound; it may be a straightforward demonstration of technique. The important thing is the *process* by which it is imparted, a process which contains many features of paracognitive support. Gradually the increasing intimacy takes on the characteristics of a collegial rather than a teacher-student relationship, and at the same time the pace and incessantness of the teaching increase. In clinical settings, the apprentice is assessed constantly for his ability, sincerity, the strength of his motivation, his commitment and maturity. The teacher takes care to monitor the rate at which he can absorb information and then proceed to integrate, incorporate, and set his own stamp upon it.

For those who prefer a more technical statement in terms of learning theory, the matter can be put this way. The student is observed to see the speed and precision with which he can take in the new knowledge, evaluate its usefulness (as defined in Bruner 1960), and then install it in his own cognitive structures. The internalization and automatization which then ensue have been described by Rapaport (1957, pp. 155–200). We add that there must simultaneously be an installation within the paracognitive support structures.

After this technical digression we must reemphasize that what is going on in this kind of learning is the sharing of knowledge. It requires intimacy, but also a kind of like-mindedness. There is an important aspect of giving, receiving, and mutuality which undergirds the entire process (reminiscent of the mother-infant symbiosis) and which, if it could be defined and measured, might be the best criterion and predictor of developmental success on this line.

At a behavioral level, as mastery is neared, the extent to which knowledge has been incorporated becomes clearer. The speed and accuracy with which it can be scanned should match the capacity and freedom to do content scanning while at the same time receiving and integrating empathically acquired knowledge. When these abilities coincide, clinical teaching and work become so effective and swift as to dazzle the unprepared observer and elude the craftiest of measurement techniques—so far. As successful integration and sequencing of cognitive and paracognitive development advances, one can observe how clinical teaching enhances in the student an avid desire for relatedness to the calling. This is a zest which may parallel but must be carefully distinguished from personal gratification in caring for patients. The latter kind of development will receive major emphasis in the next chapter, but this kind of overlapping is characteristic of the schema being advanced here, and it can be expected to occur again. Relatedness to the calling may be something of which both student and teacher are unaware, but it, too, will come up again.

The kind of education we have been describing has essential pre-conditions. The apprentice must be able to approach the senior physician in a way prescribed by tradition. Like most traditions, it persists because it is psychologically sound. It harks back in histori-cal time to the earliest traditions in medicine, and in individual ontogenetic time to early life eras when respect for and eagerness to learn from more developmentally advanced figures, usually adults, was less complicated by ambivalence and less troubled by needs to rebel. The student must also prove himself trustworthy, by demon-strating that he will know how to use the master-teacher's knowl-edge properly and, when the time comes, transmit it wisely. Here the antiquity of the calling and its rules about teaching surface once again: The obligation to share knowledge with colleagues is part of the Hippocratic oath.

Historic evidence confirms the trends and development we are putting forward. They have been part of medicine, its institutions, and its interface with society for at least three millennia, although perhaps not expressed precisely in these ways. The facts suggest two essential points: The methods work, no matter how many pejorative and poorly defined epithets are affixed to them. And there is no shortage of these. Medicine is accused of being a network of folk-ways, biases, value systems, cults, and most recently, of perpetuat-ing "the medical model." Secondly, the whole complicated system has been an integral part, if not the core, of medicine and medical education (in this sense it is difficult to disentangle the two) for so long that until recently no one has needed to inquire why and how the systems work.

It is time for another example of how they do work. One juncture at which to observe the achievement of coherent perception (a func-tion of both objectivity and empathy) is when a student approaches diagnostic assessment. We believe that as far as the perceptual as-pects of this task are concerned the important question is not whether the doctor or the doctor-to-be is aware of psychological currents. Our experiences (L. Zabarenko et al. 1968) and those of others (e.g., Greco and Pittenger 1966) indicates that most physi-cians do sense the psychological. The crucial issue is the internal level at which this information is stored. To what extent is it conscious, unconscious, preconscious? How available is it to the student or doctor and when, if at all, can the information be retrieved? During the search for a diagnosis, even a tentative one, physicians usually attempt to muster the sharpest, most complete cognitive scan possible. Where empathic capacities remain, this kind of scan need not lead to a disruption of the doctor-patient relationship or to the impersonality so much resented by patients. The student can witness in the skilled clinician, as he goes about diagnostic work, a combination of empathic and cognitive (objective) functions.

It is important here to distinguish between empathy, sympathy, and compassion. In most physicians, the latter affects are steadily maintained, but regulated to allow the doctor to remain comfortable and function effectively as the person in charge of the patient's care. *Empathy*, as we use the term, implies more diverse and subtle processes. Some kinds of empathy are used to sense the patient's general affective state, his fear, apprehension, degree of confidence in those caring for him, and much more. The kind of operative empathy of particular concern to us for this line of development is that used to react with and potentiate the cognitive knowledge already available as a result of education and data gathered from the patient.

As clinical teaching begins to dominate the curriculum, one can often observe a transformation that indicates how the student is faring in his progress toward mastery in this line. No matter how much the basic sciences may have captured the student's interest, and no matter how much mystery has been replaced with mastery, the elusiveness of definitive answers in actual medical practice and the challenge of the questions raised by this uncertainty may release a flood of empathic tendencies. One can often see this on the occasion of the first contact with patients, frequently in the course on physical diagnosis. But whenever encountered, it remains a bench mark, a place at which the student can experience for himself the fact that good medical work depends upon rapid oscillation between objectivity and empathy, especially in diagnostic assessment.

At advanced levels of mastery there is less an oscillation between empathy and objectivity than a set of integrated functions which includes both. Our guess is that what eventually becomes a smooth, seemingly effortless function may have to begin as a halting succession of swings and overswings, and go on to increasingly rapid and balanced alternation. The empathic mode of information gathering can be thought of more specifically as a set of empathic supports which let the student perceive certain aspects of the patient's condition and consider cognitive possibilities that might not otherwise be available to him. The integration of this broader range of data with the more commonly taught objective modes yields the best, that is, the most complete and satisfying results.

It would be inaccurate and graceless to leave this section without the reminder that basic science teachers make substantial contributions to developmental maturation. Such teachers are in most ways very similar to excellent clinical teachers. When a basic science instructor in medicine can retain the flexibility for both empathic and objective paracognitive approaches, he may become a great teacher, one who shares knowledge freely and joyfully. These teachers usually have little concern for institutional, territorial, or professional prerogatives because their overriding curiosity and desire to understand are so strong that they transcend these constructions. If oracularity was appealing early in their careers, as it is for most teachers, that particular gratification has faded and been transformed into the pleasures of transferring knowledge to a new academic generation and taking pride in their accomplishments. A reservoir of knowledge and skills leaves these teachers free to dispense them as passionately and energetically as their styles dictate. But the dispensation is never thoughtless or indiscriminate, for that would be wasteful. The learner is doggedly monitored so that the dose of knowledge and skills administered is bounded almost entirely by the students' limitations and stage of development and very little by the teachers' intrapsychic need to reserve some private omniscience. Clearly, the psychological essence of good teaching in clinical and basic medical science is the same. It depends upon maturation in the teacher and the learner and, of course, the match between them.

FIGURE 3

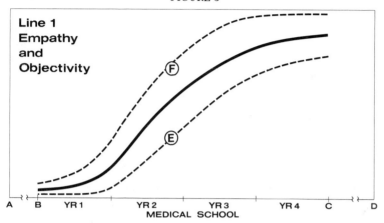

Figure 3 depicts our hypothesis about developmental progress along line 1. In this diagram we have sketched only the medical school years, since the preceding material has outlined some notions which may apply to earlier developments, points A through B, and has suggested some of the events of the consolidation years, points C through D. Circles E and F represent two students whom we have chosen to illustrate our hypothesis. Both were at the end of their sophomore year in a medical school where they had had steady, responsible contact with patients for about six months. Their work had been and would continue to be the object of careful surveillance and persistent teaching by preceptors who were full-time physician faculty members. But at the time of these incidents, the students were being encouraged to do increasing amounts of independent work, histories and physical examinations in particular. Both were about midway through the upward developmental surge.

But here the similarities end. Student E was barely within the lower educationally feasible range. Student F, already recognized as an excellent doctor-to-be, was advancing toward upper levels. He had, even at this stage, begun to elicit special efforts from his teachers whose goals, as usual, were to encourage his precocity while mounting a guard against carelessness, arrogance, or developmental gaps of any other sort.

Student E was a quiet young woman. Some of her teachers felt she was "withdrawn"; there was general agreement that she tried hard, was shy and unassertive. To at least three teachers she seemed to be chronically, if mildly depressed, but could speak of the reasons for this to no one on the faculty. The patient, Mrs. Q, was a woman in her mid-thirties, whose visits to the office for herself and her children were often as frequent as three times a week. On this occasion, she told the nurse that she had come for another adjustment in her birth control pills which she felt were causing menstrual irregularity, excessive menstrual flow, and leaving her exhausted and short of breath. She also needed to have a number of her medications checked, especially those controlling her allergies. Hers were not imagined complaints, but they were "tickets of admission" in Balint's (1964) sense. That is, for this visit as on many previous ones, they allowed Mrs. Q access to a physician, a succoring contact which she needed. She had not mentioned to the nurse the illness that was causing her the most suffering: a moderate but worsening neurotic depression.

The student, carefully following the rules she had been taught about allowing patients to tell their own stories, began by asking, "How are things going for you Mrs. Q?" The patient was not reticent. Her description of her "medical" problems was brief; she sensed the student-doctor's sympathetic receptivity. Perhaps, like many neurotic patients, she also sensed that the student-physician was coping with some depression herself, although neither participant was fully aware of it. In any case, within a few moments, Mrs. Q began to speak about one source of her sadness: a restless, defiant eighteen-year-old daughter whose truancy and cigarette smoking were just irritating enough to a rigid high-school principal to menace her graduation. The patient herself had always longed for an education, but her mother had discouraged it. Her daughter's graduation had great meaning for her, and the daughter knew it.

Having gone this far, and noting with surprise that Student E was still listening sympathetically and did not seem to need to begin a physical examination at once, Mrs. Q went on to describe more deep-seated, long-standing problems. Her relationship to her divorced mother had always been tortuously ambivalent. Now nearing her sixties, her mother had become demanding and petulantly dependent. Mrs. Q also worried about another daughter of thirteen who she feared was "going wild" and would soon be uncontrollable. Mr. Q was described as an energetic and loving man, filled with plans for family projects which called for more work than his wife felt she could manage. She was desperately fearful that she might disappoint him.

By this time, thirty minutes had passed. Mrs. Q had grown steadily more depressed, agitated, apprehensive, and tearful. The student, empathically absorbed, one is tempted to say locked, into the situation, unable to move to an objective or executive stance, began to look very sad herself, though she remained composed.

At this moment the instructor knocked on the door of the examining room. A glance at the sobbing patient and the sober student was enough for him to guess what had happened. He informed Student E that the waiting room was filling with patients and asked if Mrs. Q's physical exmaination had been completed. There was an edge of irritation in the teacher's inquiry, hardly surprising under the circumstances, and from an educational point of view, the interruption had a salutory effect. Rather than using empathy as a tool for data gathering, the student had become enmeshed in an excessive, sympathetic identification with the patient. She was not able to step back and consider the patient's story as data of great potential value for the treatment. The instructor's intervention jarred her loose, and she could then go on to the examination, conducting it at a level of skill appropriate to her training. Within ten minutes Student E reported back to the instructor with the results.

Like all illustrative examples from the extremes, this one displays rather dramatically what poor patient care can result when there is a retardation of the development of the ability to alternate and combine objectivity and empathy. However, the example may seem overdrawn, exaggerated. Objections could be raised that the student may have been only occasionally or temporarily vulnerable to derailment in this way and does not deserve to be placed at the brink of educability. But there is more evidence.

After the examination findings for Mrs. Q had been verified, Student E and the preceptor discussed her medications and problems with her, and she agreed to a psychiatric referral. Then attempts at teaching began. The preceptor was able to reconstruct the events of the original half-hour encounter only with difficulty. He questioned Student E carefully, extracting bits of coherent information from her brief, usually monosyllabic answers. Feeling more compassionate now, but bent upon trying to trace the student's difficulty, the doctor asked if she had any idea how she had got "into this situation." Eyes averted, she shook her head. The preceptor elected not to pursue the issue of Student E's own depression as a possible etiology for the difficulty. He began, instead, a brief but intense series of explanations: (1) the importance of balances in the doctor-patient relationship; (2) the fact that continuing patient care enables the doctor to make good therapeutic use of repeated brief contacts rather than necessarily lengthy ones; and (3) how crucial it is to recognize the need and opportunity for psychiatric referrals speedily—if arrangements can be made on the spot, patients are often comforted by the knowledge that help is on the way, and the primary-care physician can temporarily delegate some aspects of the therapeutic work and go on to treat other patients. Throughout this articulate, well-conceived teaching effort, Student E avoided making eye contact. At first she sat immobile, but gradually began to fidget. At last the teacher, feeling defeated, and probably rightly so, asked if she understood what he was saying. Murmuring a barely audible, "I think so," she was swiftly up from her chair and out of the room, leaving the preceptor to wonder what other methods of approach he might have used and what the eventual course of things would be.

We have already described Student F as advanced and hardworking. At the end of his sophomore year, the time of this incident, he had taken on the care of more people than most of his peers had. He always seemed willing, even when weary, to see yet another unscheduled patient or to check up for himself on the hospital care of patients with whom he was working. In the primary-care office, his co-workers, nurses, laboratory technicians, and preceptors had begun to know something of his strengths and excellences and to count on them and him.

The episode we have chosen concerns Mrs. W, who was new to the service. Student F and his preceptor had treated her successfully for two bouts of pneumonia within as many months. During these visits the patient was often very ill or weak, and the doctors had concentrated on her major problems. There had been no time for any history but that limited to the immediate and urgent disease processes. But they had encouraged Mrs. W to return for a complete health evaluation when she was well, and this task was assigned to Student F.

It soon came out that, at thirty-one, Mrs. W had spent much of her life in hospitals. She had had nine major surgical procedures, including removal of one lobe of each lung. Since the age of three she had had pulmonary infections, usually pneumonia, three to four times a year, "never less than three, doctor." As Student F moved systematically through her history, he discovered that there were no areas in which Mrs. W had not experienced or was not now experiencing substantial medical problems. After taking a lengthy history of her long-standing pulmonary difficulties, he moved to the endocrine system to discover that she had been diagnosed as hyperthyroid at age twelve but the condition had never been properly managed. When he inquired about the gastrointestinal system, she described in detail the latest x-rays of her gastric ulcer, which was under intermittent but basically poor control. Yes, she had indeed had difficulty with muscles and joints and routinely suffered aches and pains in all the major joints of her body.

Without very much in the way of warning, Student F had come upon a patient with an Olympian collection of medical problems, any one of which might have constituted a serious management problem. In addition, though at the time of this examination she was as healthy as one might reasonably expect under the circumstances, Mrs. W was plainly depressed. And there were some puzzling if promising inconsistencies in the psychosocial history. In spite of

years of ill health she had had two obstetrically unremarkable de-
liveries. This was a point of great pride for her, for despite warnings
that the births would have to be Caesarean, the fetuses were small
and normal delivery had been possible. She was proud of the fact
that the children were "perfectly healthy" and spoke with a flicker of
enthusiasm about her hobby—the breeding, raising, and training of
large dogs—her pleasure in riding, and her expectation that she
would soon have a horse of her own.

This description could be extended further, but the main point is
the effect it had upon the student. Taking his usual thorough and
meticulous history he soon found his notebook bulging, for Mrs. W
was exquisitely well informed on the precise diagnoses (or lack
thereof) of her disorders, the medications that had been tried successfully and unsuccessfully, and the nature and intensity of the
disagreements among the medical specialists who had treated her.
She had, after all, spent three decades in persistent contact with
medical personnel and institutions. Student F was beginning to feel
deluged. As he turned from one organ system to another, his hope
that he would uncover at least one disease-free system was palpable.
But he had no such luck. In spite of this, he showed no impatience,
listened carefully and empathically to the patient's comments and
recorded as much as he could. It is a testimonial to the extent to
which he had already begun to organize disease systems and history
taking that he could conclude this history in about fifty minutes.

The patient was an experienced doctor-watcher, and his
thoroughness and forbearance were not lost on her. A nonpartici-
pant preceptor had been in the room during the history taking. At its
conclusion, Mrs. W looked over the student's head at the teacher
and said with the faintest of smiles, "He's going to be a good one,
isn't he?"

In the teaching that followed this episode Student F and his
preceptors had time to speak at some length about what it must
mean to be multiply ill from an early age, how this must affect this
woman's relationships to her family of origin and to her husband and
children. Her nonchildhood ("I can honestly never remember being

a child, doctor, I can only remember being sick") must surely have great psychological significance. It was one of the factors considered in the attempts to understand her depression.

But the point of greatest importance for our purposes was Student F's reaction to the whole unsettling experience. Though understandably overwhelmed, he was also challenged, and at least overtly neither angry nor irritated with the patient for being so ill and for having diseases which were probably not curable. The word *crock,* the physician's customary, pejorative admission of defeat, was never used in the discussion. The student's main concern was that he might have revealed his fear and dismay as each new pathological constellation hove into view and that this concern might have alarmed Mrs. W. With real urgency he asked his teachers, "Just what is a good way to handle that situation?"

From the developmental point of view, this student dealt with a difficult situation, calling for an alternation and combination of operative empathy, compassion, and painstaking, objective fact-gathering in such a way as to impress even an experienced patient, probably the most critical judge of medical care extant. His preceptors were pleased with his work, but did their best to concentrate upon ways in which it might be even more efficient and complete. Another important sign of advanced development, if one were needed, is the fact that the student's main concern was whether he had managed his empathic and objective functions adequately.

These clinical examples are meant to emphasize but in no way distract from the theoretical proposals. The first developmental line has very deep historical and ontogenetic roots. Perhaps this is one of the reasons that it surges up first. The second line is no less venerable; it, too, draws upon early life experiences in every doctor and doctor-to-be. But there are some new twists, and this is not an accidental metaphor. We are presenting each line separately because that seems the best way to begin. But as we have said, and will continue to reiterate, these developmental trends no sooner emerge than they begin to intertwine, like the roots of a tree. Living systems such as physicianhood are complicated, but this is the attribute that makes them so exciting and aesthetically beautiful. If this sounds romantic, we offer reassurance from a distinguished colleague and friend: "The marriage of imagination and reality is the only romance a scientist can enter into legitimately" (Shevrin 1976, p. 2). We have at least four more romances to pursue.

CHAPTER 4

Developmental Line 2: Appropriate Management of Nurturance and Executive Necessity

The concepts necessary to the discussion of this line are frequently clouded by out-of-date or simplified connotations. We emphasized above that nurturant tendencies may at first be associated with female figures in early life—mother, grandmothers, older sisters, etc. But the wish to take care of others is also present in males, although there are large differences in style. Cultural factors, by no means static, have affected and will continue to affect the way in which needs to nurture are expressed. We also pointed out that there are unique residuals of the oedipal period in physicians. This is supported by evidence from observing physicians at work (Nunberg 1938; L. Zabarenko et al. 1968), information from the analytic treatment of physicians (Glauber 1953; R. Zabarenko et al. 1970), and observations of children (S. Freud 1905, Simmel 1926).

These two facets, nurturant tendencies in both sexes and unique developmental residuals in doctors, suggest that the major precursors of this line come from a period later than those giving rise to line 1. Line 2 apparently springs from a period where caretaking and those who do it are the focus of attention. In center stage is the question of the gender of nurturant figures and how their ways of nurturing differ. Parents are the figures children observe most closely, but the family doctor may also be available for them to watch at work. Preschool children may be frightened by this figure, but his power and mysteriousness make him an object of fascination as well.

Caretaking roles in Western culture are still in most places assigned to women; for some children this role assignment can be conflictual. Boys who want to take care of people may discover that the idea is derogated as effeminate, the opposite of being a "real boy." The role can have both attractive and repulsive characteristics. Girls who feel drawn to its gratifying aspects may fear it puts them in danger of exploitation or subservience. For us the most important thing is that small children, caught up in these dilemmas and busy thinking about them at a level appropriate to their age, may find a solution in the idea of being a doctor. Medicine is a calling which embodies a way of nurturing with societal sanction and with both masculine and feminine identifications present, active and varied.

In latency and adolescence the longing for nurturant activities can sometimes be allowed to surface as devotion to animals, small children, or machines. In girls these tendencies are often culturally syntonic and thus less conflicted. Boys frequently solve the problem by synthesis; they give nurturing an active, masculine cast by placing themselves in charge, by being the person responsible for making sure that adequate care is given. This role is apt to evoke praise and approval for the adolescent, and may be one of the important substrates of physicianhood.

Predictably, the extent to which adolescents find nurturant tendencies accepted can vary enormously. For some, internal and environmental hurdles to acknowledging these feelings produce substantial turbulence in which the adolescent may need to repudiate (unconsciously) his wishes to be nurturant by turning them round, becoming extremely self-concerned or concerned with his own body exclusively. There may also be a retreat from caretaking of any kind. The result of this conviction, often vehemently held, is that the body per se is of no importance and must be ignored or even abused. In other young people concern with their own bodies becomes a devotion to perfecting them. The thirteen-year-old boy working with weights and jogging one hour each day, or the fifteen-year-old girl who lavishes time and money on every detail of her appearance, are examples of what we mean. Their nurturant needs have been deflected at least temporarily from others and focused upon themselves. They are taking care of someone in a special way by concentrating on their own bodies so as to make them more beautiful and more gender specific, i.e., stereotypically masculine or feminine. In this way they avoid or postpone coming to grips with their need to care for others.

All of these varieties of repudiation and distortion are the result of the potentiation of conflicts about nurturance by newly emergent sexuality. Often a whole spectrum of drives is, in a psychological sense, forced underground until it can be better understood and the internal controls perfected for dealing with it. Nurturance is frequently inhibited with the rest. In healthy development, these drives reemerge and recombine later in different forms and with less intensity.

Such features of general development have special importance for our thesis, because the resurgence of nurturance in young adulthood is likely to be occurring in medical students at about the same time as their training is getting underway. If the expected regression has not lasted too long or gone too deep, time and maturation will result in adequate and gratifying nurturant functioning in the adult. This is most directly seen in the actual comforting of someone in distress. A special version of this, and one which turns out to be a precursor of physicianhood, contains this kind of comforting but also includes certain executive functions. The executive necessities in medicine subsume a number of characteristics. The individual must be responsible, decisive, active, willing to be the person in charge, capable of bearing the fact that he or she may be the person who will inflict pain in order to produce cure and also the person who works upon another's body. These characteristics derive for the most part from the masculine developmental spheres. They are the opposite of the ingathering, containing, comforting, feeding aspects of the feminine spheres. This is the core meaning of the title of this development line: both nurturant tendencies and executive necessities must come to be managed.

We can outline the early precursors of this phase as follows. As an infant and toddler, the child is cared for. If this is done happily and is mutually gratifying to parents and child, such a child tends to include the caretaking function in its own developing personality in

many different ways. Even in these early stages, two currents in
development are commingled: (1) the idea of caring for, comforting,
and succoring; and (2) the idea of doing this via active, appropriate,
and responsible actions. Sometimes through latency and adolescence there emerges a kind of intellectualized compassion-
nurturance. This is often encouraged and buttressed by moral institutions, both internal, that is, the conscience, and external, for
example, the ethical values represented by religious or cultural institutions. During these years one may also see a reversal of the wish
to comfort. The cruelty which nine- and ten-year-old boys can show
to their peers, and especially to those who may be ill, appalls adult
sensitivities. Temporarily there is an inability to deal with the wish
to nurture, and the need is turned inside out. In this period one can
also see other manifestations which exemplify partial solutions to the
question of how to deal with the simultaneous wishes to nurture and
to be responsible. Some young people during latency and adolescence fear suffering or feel helpless when faced with it in others.
They need to escape from acknowledging its existence or at least
from witnessing its effects. These trials and partial solutions are
necessary and developmentally sound. In Western culture children
at this age for the most part do not have access yet to the solutions
that will ultimately work in adult life. Any given child may experience some or all of these partial solutions, and the outcomes of such
trials may support later the professionally sanctioned implementation of nurturant behavior in medical work.

We have described a range of experiences that most children pass
through in the period before medical training begins. Those who
will become physicians (as well as others) move from the position of
care-receiver to that of care-giver. The special kinds of early experiences each has had will result in different styles of physicianhood,
the choice of different specialties, and different modes of delivery of
care.

Since these developmental previews are familiar, and since each
young person also follows unique patterns of growth, it is natural to
ask, "What is it that crystallizes the desire for physicianhood in some
and not in others?" The answer is that often one cannot know. But

we can present two instances of physicians in whom it was possible to trace the route. In both, the decision to become a doctor was related to intense, early, traumatic experiences involving the bodies of nuclear family members. We believe such experiences may be a turning point for many who become physicians. In one case the evidence comes from analytic treatment; in the second, it was available via thoughtful reminiscence and reflection. The selection of these two sources is not accidental. These and other sources of information need to be utilized increasingly to answer one of the questions underlying all these developmental lines, Why medicine? We believe the information so gained can shed some real light upon the perennial problems of how to select and train physicians in such a way as to produce the best medical care and the most gratification for those who provide it.

As a result of memories recovered during his own psychoanalysis, a distinguished psychiatrist was able to recapture the moment of the first internal decision to become a physician. When he was four, his younger sister, of whom he was very fond, became ill, and a rural doctor managed her illness so badly that she nearly died. "Then and there," he said, "although I did not realize it till years later, I decided that I would become a doctor, and when I did, I would do it right." The reconstruction of this moment of personal history was vivid. In fact, knowing the man, one could almost picture him, a sturdy, active four-year-old, setting his jaw with determination in a manner still characteristic of him years later.

But such decisions are never as beguilingly simple as they may sound. Consider, for example, the number of factors involved in this instance: there is focus on the body, in this case that of a sibling; the young boy's devotion to his sister; and his age- and phase-appropriate competitiveness with a bungling father-equivalent physician. At age four, most boys are thoroughly engaged in the issues of the oedipal conflict, including feelings of rivalry with and admiration of authority figures and caring persons—mother, father, doctor, or all three. In this case another determinant was the little boy's outrage that this sister's body, which he considered precious and until that time perfect, had been imperiled. Nor can we overlook the possibility of ambivalence in his feelings toward his sister. His identification with her and her danger must have added emphasis to the episode and to its crucial influence in his life.

In our second example, a pediatrician was asked if he knew when he first wanted to become a physician. At first he said he could not remember ever wanting to be anything else. It is our guess when one hears this commonly expressed sentiment it means that the desire to be a doctor has some of its roots in early events before the time of continuous memory, and these components coalesce later into the vocational choice. Having made the initial, familiar statement, this particular physician reflected a few minutes and said he thought that probably the question had been settled for him in pubescence. When he was twelve, his parents were involved in two serious automobile accidents. To his great good fortune the physicians who cared for them sympathized with the boy's loneliness, looked after him, and in a way, took him in as a member of their group. By making him a kind of mascot, they provided affection and age-appropriate nurturance which sustained him through a difficult time and pleased them. It may also have provided a chance to relive a phase in their own development in a happier way.

The experience was a crucial preparatory phase for this man's career. Because the doctors admitted him to their circle, he was actually able to watch as the bodies of his parents were repaired and restored to health. As in the previous case, the matter was not settled by this single episode; there were other factors determining his choice of profession. But the time spent as part of a temporary, extended family of physicians solidified the assimilation of earlier internal psychological events and confirmed his wish to be a doctor.

As doctors, both of these men were keen observers, and so they were as children. They had the chance to see firsthand that doctors could heal and nurture, that they enjoyed it, and that the work involved no sacrifice of self-respect. This was an especially important point for boys growing up forty years ago; it may be of less concern now. We think it likely that both young boys also perceived clearly, although they probably could not have put it into words, that responsible activity and nurturance were a core of physician-hood. Both aspects were appealing; in these cases magnetic.

We have written at some length about the precursors for this line because it is important to establish them developmentally and show how they are similar to and distinct from those which undergird line 1. During the medical school years, line 2 shoots up less rapidly than that described for the empathy-objectivity coalition (see figure 4). In part, this is because empathy is a complex of affective processes. Once these feelings can be released or disinhibited, they can soon be experienced and expressed, often during the transition from basic science to clinical habitats. But mastery of the nurturant-executive family of tasks is quite a different matter. For this developmental line, the transition from basic science to clinical work is a period of slow progress. At this point the meaning of being the ultimately responsible nurturant figure with its awesome consequences as well as its heady gratifications becomes quite graphic. The student, until now restrained, is released, told that he may in a sense "take possession of" the body of a patient.

Paracognitive structures are usually not yet adequate for a com-

FIGURE 4

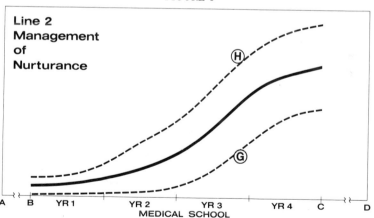

fortable assumption of full responsibility, and the student is quite properly permitted to retreat. Sometimes the route of retreat is to seek safety in learning thoroughly, even meticulously, small slices of medicine, a regression into scientism. In another delaying maneuver, students may at first perform the nurturant task bit by bit in a firmly structured manner. Afraid that they may harm the patient, they return to an earlier and antiquated style of intellective approach because it seems to offer protection against the consequences of error. Legions of medical school instructors have witnessed sensitive, compassionate students become tongue-tied, awkward and obsessionally concerned with problem lists and system orientations in the earliest confrontations with patients. This will happen even when these involve only a routine physical examination and ample protective faculty backup is available. Medical school professors also lament that students who have been assiduously taught what constitutes a thorough physical examination and who may have even responded correctly to a cognitive test on the subject cannot perform the task (at first) when faced with a live patient. The same problems come up in taking an adequate history. The task seems overwhelming, and the student backs off by focusing on narrow areas because they seem manageable and safer.

One possible explanation for these learning difficulties, which are in most cases temporary, is to be found in the psychological evolution we have been discussing. The first patient contacts call for activation of nurturance and executive responsibility, but the student may not yet have sufficient integrated and conflict-free nurturant-executive capacities to support the medical task. As training begins and maturation and confidence ensue, the push of development in this phase begins.

The critical period for this line extends beyond medical school for some physicians. During the period, however long, the student-physician is often in the grip of a kind of all-or-none conviction which, though powerful, may not be expressed. He comes to believe that full perception of the patient, as reflected in a thorough examination and adequate history, will require full care of all aspects of the patient's health and even happiness. The ability to separate these two functions, perception and care, diagnosis and treatment, is one sign that mastery may be at hand. At the same time, and slowly, the work begins to change from a particulated performance to a smoother, more comfortable, and more encompassing approach to the task. These two behavioral pairs, perception and care, diagnosis and treatment, match the two developmental lines thus far described: empathy and objectivity; nurturance and activity.

A corollary of impending mastery is the capacity to sequence the two functions in time. Observation of the extent to which the student-physician can allow himself fullest access to information about the patient, use the broadest possible perceptual scan, and integrate what he perceives into a synthesis of the patient's feelings, will give some gauge of development. The broadest possible perceptual scan includes data from empathic as well as cognitive sources. Only in this way can adequate comprehension of the patient's condition result. But the intimate, complex, and ongoing relation between empathy and cognition remains largely unexplored. Although we cannot say exactly how it happens, when this kind of data gathering and adequate regulation of need to care responsibly can govern the physician's relatedness to the patient, mastery is imminent. The student who feels that he must do everything and be everything to the patient or "turn off," still has some distance to travel. As students can comfortably await an adequate diagnosis and proceed with treatment using the data at hand, developmental progress accelerates. When the unspoken imperative that to perceive everything requires that one must do everything for the patient can be resisted fully, clinical judgment is emergent.

This process is worked out in successive stages. One can think of maturation of clinical judgment as the increasing capacity to be able to care responsibly in the absence of perceiving everything and in the face of the possibility of not being able to do anything, let alone everything. Perhaps the ability to exercise these restraints sounds elementary, something one might reasonably expect in any mature, rational adult. But even mature individuals struggle with irrational thoughts and feelings; being able to sustain these particular kinds of control represents one specific and unique requirement of physicianhood. It is a difficult and significant maturational hurdle. When a physician-in-training can treat a patient in the absence of knowing as much as he would like to, or as much as he feels he needs to, this is a signal that an advanced stage has been reached. Other signals are the capacities to: (1) do as much as is possible for the patient at any given point in the doctor-patient relationship, (2) maintain that relationship even though what is done is less than optimal, and (3) sustain the relationship even though the obstacles which prevent the best care may be poorly understood aspects of the patient and the physician himself. Clues about how far along an individual is in these steps of professional maturation can be picked up by observing the capacity to understand patients and to make use of the skills, knowledge, and mastery of colleagues to assist in the nurturance-executive task.

The ultimate site at which to assess mastery for this line, as for all five, is clinical performance. At their best, nurturant tendencies can be a wellspring for the physician's life-preserving drive, a psychic core for his activities. But they must be mediated and tempered by, and combined with, rationality and cognitive discipline. When this development does not come to full fruition there are difficulties with certain kinds of patients. Those with terminal or chronic illnesses, for example, become particularly hard to deal with. If we assume that the doctor's goal, perhaps conscious, perhaps not, is to restore the body of the patient to health, i.e., to perfection of function and attractiveness, the certainty that the patient will die can become painful. And the stress is especially acute when death occurs slowly with accompanying disfigurement and gradual loss of function in spite of the doctor's best efforts. In many chronic diseases, cure is impossible and success must be measured in terms of the amount of stability that can be achieved. Such doctor-patient relationships constitute a large chunk of medical practice, and the styles in which the stresses of these relationships are sustained merit much more investigation than they have received. Working with the dying and the chronically ill, many doctors are frustrated, impatient, and find it necessary to distance themselves psychologically from their pa-tients. This represents a distortion of the executive functions even though nurturant activities continue. At worst these feelings may cloud judgment; at best, faced and understood, they can lead to more comfort for the doctor, and better care for the patient.

The situation is complicated by the fact that the doctor is expected not only to fight disease, but also to represent and exemplify health. Such patient expectations may not be reasonable, but most practicing physicians acknowledge they exist and constitute an urgent psychological need. Doctors accept this aspect of their image and role with varying degrees of awareness. There are also instances where doctors have had a disease but are making a strong stand against it.

Strategies for styling practice to cope with these stresses are as varied as the doctors themselves. It is possible, for example, to select a specialty which will reduce substantially the likelihood of being responsible for the management of the terminal or chronically ill patient. Pathology, dermatology, and plastic surgery are examples of such specialities; primary medical care is closer to the other end of the spectrum. But no matter what specialty or practice style, there is danger of failure of judgment when discouragement cuts deep enough to penetrate the paracognitive support apparatus and enters the personal rather than the professional zone of the physician's psyche. This is a contingency which the traditions of medicine make some provision for. The Hippocratic oath specifically enjoins against the treatment of family or close relatives. Experienced physicians know that there are other situations fraught with hazards. Here, perhaps, a clinical vignette will help—an example of successful management of the failure of mastery in this developmental line.

The patient was a fifty-six-year-old man who had been in and out of the hospital for two and one-half months with acute anginal symptoms. After some delay, coronary angiography was done, and coronary bypass surgery, considered mandatory, was performed successfully. The patient was discharged with no complications and a remission of symptoms. Three days later he suffered an attack of paroxysmal auricular tachycardia, with a heart rate around 250 beats per minute. There was a history of this disturbance since adolescence.

The physician in this case, Dr. I, was an internist who had cared for the patient since both had graduated from medical school thirty-one years before. Classmates, best friends, and colleagues, each had seen the other and his family through a number of medical crises. The life-threatening illness of his good friend had, until this time, been managed by Dr. I, but at some cost. He had been unwilling, for example, to accept the judgment of the first three cardiologists who consulted on the case that serious coronary problems existed. Dr. I's position was that the data suggested a more cautious diagnosis: mild myocardial infarction. Finally, the evidence became conclusive and the necessity for an angiogram clear. Dr. I viewed and studied the films extensively. In the period between the angiogram and the surgery the patient experienced daily bouts of severe anginal pain in the coronary care unit at bed rest. At one time during these stressful days, Dr. I stood in the corridor talking to the patient's family. His facial expression and demeanor were such that a colleague coming by, stopped and interrupted the conversation to ask, "Is a member of your family in the unit? I hope all goes well." Dr. I said openly that although he had advised a number of patients to have this kind of surgery performed, he never had "gone through it" himself until his friend fell ill.

On the occasion of the postsurgical tachycardia, Dr. I and the patient's wife met in the emergency room as they had a number of times in the preceding months. She made a feeble attempt at humor. "Sam, we can't go on meeting like this." The expression on Dr. I's face altered, and he announced that he was turning the management of the case over to the cardiologists, feeling that he no longer had "sufficient judgment to manage things properly." The attack lasted six and one-half hours. Dr. I stayed with his friend, cancelled rounds at two hospitals and an afternoon of appointments, and asked a colleague to cover emergency calls.

The vignette speaks to our point eloquently enough. Dr. I, recognizing a temporary failure in his capacity to keep nurturant and executive capacities in proper balance, abdicated his physicianhood. He did not abdicate his friendship, and his relinquishment of his responsibilities as a doctor was temporary. He resumed the care of the patient through the convalescence with confidence. But he was capable of realizing when the weakening of usual paracognitive support systems (after repeated battering) had resulted in an intrusion into a personal and emotionally charged area of his personality and might impair his function as a professional.

There are a variety of modes (some might say defenses) by which doctors come to manage the balance required. Not all physicians are stressed by similar problems. There are some who intentionally take on the care of the chronically ill and dying and others who are reluctant to deal with a whole body even when it is no longer alive. Some doctors choose geriatrics, or the care of the critically ill, trauma and emergency medicine; some become coroners, and there are pathologists who are uncomfortable or even unwilling to perform autopsies, doing clinical pathology instead.

It is also true that most doctors feel enormous gratification when they can quickly transform someone in pain and beset by illness into a person once again fully functioning and free of discomfort. In a previous research project we observed this kind of doctor-patient transaction often enough to designate it as a category and give it a name: the emergency transaction. There was enough data to construct a prototypical picture, a sort of holograph, of the dynamics of these encounters. We observed emergency transactions relatively rarely in the offices of primary-care physicians. But it seems likely that similar feelings occur in surgical specialties like the restorative cardiovascular surgery described for Dr. I's friend and patient. On these occasions the doctor can repair damage, may be able to alleviate pain and life threat, and do these things swiftly and conclusively. It can be no surprise that these procedures, a source of substantive gratification, have special appeal for medical students.

Another mode of incomplete mastery in this developmental line can be observed in the attitude of physicians toward those patients who may remain disfigured or functionally impaired even though a medical or surgical procedure has preserved their lives. It cannot be coincidental, for example, that both mastectomy and colostomy patients have banded together as lay groups, i.e., the Reach for Recovery Organization, for postoperative support and adjustment. Nor can it be without significance that those suffering from alcoholism, obesity, and some kinds of psychiatric disorders have formed self-help groups. We propose that these patients, alive but permanently impaired by a physician's work or afflicted with diseases for which no really effective treatment exists, turn to each other because they cannot receive the kind of supportive help they need from their doctors. Other patients, for example, those who have undergone appendectomies or cholecystectomies, have felt no need to form supportive postoperative groups.

The choice of medical specialty, revealing on several counts, can also portray something of the relationship of paracognitive strands to cognitive mastery in this line of development. For those who have chosen primary care as their area of physicianhood, flexibility about and comfort with an appropriately monitored balance of nurturant tendencies and executive responsibilities needs to be at its maximum. With specialization and subspecialization come different solutions to the problem. The physician remains the ultimately re-sponsible nurturant figure, but the fields of knowledge and the illnesses within which he is operative are smaller. Pediatric cardiol-ogy, peripheral vascular surgery, and the many subspecialties in hematology and endocrinology are illustrations. Physicians function-ing in these fields may feel with some justification that the expansion of knowledge requires the limitation of their work field. They must restrict their range so that they are able to heal where others cannot.

Lest there be any misunderstanding, we are not inferring that work in a specialty or subspecialty requires less complete mastery of this paracognitive line of development; nor do we imply any con-striction or defect in competence or personality. But mastery has a different quality. In specialties and subspecialties there is often in-creased reliance on colleagues. The team concept is vital to running a successful neonatology unit or the maintenance of a nephrology service for patients who need to use the kidney dialysis machine. In these specialties physicians have indeed been able to share nurtur-ant and executive functions.

To recapitulate: For the second line of development we have presented hypotheses and data about precursors, the phenomena of the critical stage and consolidation period, and the modes by and extent to which cognitive and paracognitive systems interrelate. The two examples of developmental progress we have chosen are represented as G and H in figure 4 above.

Student G, nearing the end of his junior year, was asked to describe the patient. "She's great," he said, "a marvelous lady." Further inquiry revealed that Mrs. N was eighty-two, suffered from uncontrolled diabetes mellitus, moderate to severe hypertension, and poor hearing. After this brief problem description, Mr. G reiterated what was for him the core of his patient, that despite her age and infirmities, she was courageous, uncomplaining, grateful for any attention, and "able to take care of herself." With this preview, student and preceptor went to the examining room.

Mrs. N had been brought to the doctor by her daughter, Mrs. L. The rapport between student-doctor and patient was obvious, but so were some less promising developments. After five weeks, four visits to the doctor, and some conferences with the dietitian, Mrs. N still had blood sugar levels far above healthy ranges, and her blood pressure remained elevated. An ulcer of the foot, not mentioned in the preliminary review, was beginning to heal. Her hearing aid worked only if it was placed directly over her sternum, turned up to its highest level, and the speaker's lips remained about two inches from it. Her daughter reported a new symptom, brief "fainting spells." Sometimes as she sat watching television or at dinner, Mrs. N would slump over; at other times she would fall, but usually regained consciousness rapidly so that no injuries occurred. Mrs. L was also concerned about her mother's climbing habits. Knowing that sweets were kept in the top kitchen cabinets, the agile Mrs. N had taken to clambering up on the counters so as to get a better look at the fastening devices used to secure the doors. Her daughter feared that a fall from this height might be dangerous, especially if her mother suffered a "fainting spell" while on her perch.

Student G's history taking and physical examination were adequate and expeditious. In the preceptor's office, he was asked about his treatment plans and replied that he would like to see the patient in another week, to check urine and blood pressure and ask

Mrs. L to continue to watch the diet carefully. When asked his opinion about the disturbances in consciousness, he replied that he felt there was little point in investigating these, as they were most probably "just another sign of senility." The hearing deficit had not been carefully assessed, nor the hearing aid checked, and Mr. G had no plans to do so. When questioned about the patient's efforts to get into the cabinets, the student chuckled, but on more serious consideration said he thought the only solution to this problem was to ask the daughter to maintain even more vigilance.

This episode illustrates flawed maturation in the developmental line in which nurturance and responsible activity need to be interwoven. Student G was in some ways very nurturant; he was clearly a psychological support for the patient. She sensed that he was concerned about her, and they enjoyed their contact with one another. We would speculate that the student's admiration of the woman, one manifestation of his nurturance, had resulted in his seeing her inaccurately, as more competent than she really was. This misperception had blocked the exhibition of responsible medical activity, so that her major medical problems had not been adequately attended to. Furthermore, the student had no plans to investigate her new and significant symptoms nor had he conducted what ought to have been a routine check of the hearing prosthesis. In brief, responsible activity was very far below optimal.

Brought up short by the preceptor's questions and comments, Student G could shift quickly into an active mode. He began to think of ways in which some of the new problems might be investigated, including the use of an audiologist for the hearing deficit and a psychometrician for assessing organic brain damage. For these reasons, he is depicted in figure 4 as within educable ranges but below the developmental average.

In this doctor-patient contract we observed another kind of lapse, a specific kind of deficiency in the capacity for the broadest possible perceptual scan of which we have spoken earlier. The key to proper medical care for Mrs. N was her daughter. The student, focused upon and charmed by the older woman, had failed to perceive that Mrs. L also had serious health problems. Her obesity and shortness of breath were apparent. From time to time during her mother's examination she would rise from her chair to shout into the hearing aid and each time she moved, would wince with pain. In fact she even mentioned that her arthritis had been particularly troublesome of late, but the student never noticed. When asked, it became very clear that he did not perceive these problems as falling within his domain. This was in a sense a double fault. As a family physician, all members of the family must be of concern, and it was especially important in this case since he was planning to have part of his executive responsibility carried out by the daughter. Responsible care of Mrs. N was important for itself and as a crucial component of the care of her mother.

Student H, also nearing the end of his junior year, was asked to "follow" hospitalized patients whom he had examined in preceptors' offices. This student had already been identified as a superior physician-to-be, but the way in which he took on the task of hospital checking confirmed the judgment. Faculty reported that, unlike most juniors required to perform this task, Mr. H made it a point to visit the patients daily during their hospital stay, even though this frequency had never been specifically requested. Not surprisingly his relationships with the patients were excellent, and his contacts with nurses and hospital-based physicians, both faculty and nonfaculty, matured rapidly with evident mutual respect and support. Said one preceptor, "Mr. H always seems to be on top of the situation, yet he never loses his sense of humor or his sense of perspective." Student H had acquired a habit which impressed everyone: He had requested that the floor nurses not discharge any of "his patients" until he had an opportunity to check with them, make sure about the next office appointment, review plans for convalescent care, and visit with the family. Honoring this request was an acknowledgment of the student's desire to learn. It could hardly be considered a requisite for medical care, since both the attending physician and a resident would already have checked the patient prior to discharge. Looking at H's record, one faculty member remarked, "He is indeed a good student at this point. I am wondering how and what more we may hope to teach him in his senior year."

This student was at the upper limits of educability in this line of development, already causing his teachers to think of him as an instructional challenge. It was not his devotion to learning or to patient care alone which was impressive; it was the fact that he felt accountable for making certain about the patient's condition and was mature enough to realize that a bridge between hospital and office care is indispensable. His active assumption of responsibility and his concern for effective doctor-patient relationships were evidence that nurturant behavior had become closely meshed with responsibility in a way representing unusual progress at this developmental and educational level.

CHAPTER 5

Developmental Line 3: Omnipotence, Omniscience, and the Toleration of Uncertainty

The power and knowledge held by the physician may fetch him hatred, admiration, envy, love, or mixtures of all of these feelings. No discussion of medicine, delivery of care, or doctor-patient relationships fails to touch upon this topic: the power and knowledge of the physician.

As in the preceding two lines of development, the precursors for this one go back to very early life experiences which are adjacent to and overlap those forming the groundwork for other lines. A careful distinction between nurturance and omnipotence is important so as to curtail muddling and encourage thinking about several aspects of the problem simultaneously. Nurturance is a set of affective and cognitive relations with others whose sources are located in the matrix of early parent-child experiences. Omnipotence is a characteristic mode of thought in infancy and in a sense is the only world view possible in an organism which has not yet established a notion of the world as distinct from itself. The belief of infants and young children that their needs and wants control or ought to control everything around them can be observed by parents, teachers, or anyone interested in young creatures. The technical term often used for this phenomenon, infantile omnipotence, is a succinct expression of the internal state of affairs. In healthy development this conviction is tempered gradually by reality during the toddler years and is a usable personality function by the time the child begins first grade.

But the regulation of the need for power is a persistent theme in growth. One variation that has special importance in the life history of those who become physicians concerns the link between power and knowledge. As always, there is a range of individual variation in the way this link is perceived. For some, power via knowledge has great appeal; others find the power ensured by manipulation or physical strength more attractive. Physicians and those who will become physicians fall in the former group. Residuals of early personality development, about which little is known, make the maintenance of power and control very important for them, and knowledge the favored route.

Data from cultural and medical anthropology tend to confirm these propositions. Medicine men in most cultures are viewed as possessing enormous power, stemming primarily from a special knowledge of spells, chants, devices, and therapeutic tools which qualify them to intervene between their patients and death. It is easy to understand why such a position, acknowledged by custom and buttressed by the belief that they alone possess life-preserving knowledge, makes medicine men in many ways as powerful as tribal leaders. No matter how exalted his status, even a chieftan might need someone to intervene between him and illness or death.

There is further cross-cultural evidence relating to this line and to the preceding one, the management of nurturance and responsibility. Many societies differentiate between two healing figures, the medicine man and the shaman. The medicine man is omniscient, powerful, and can be frightening. The shaman has a more intimate and in some cases constant role in the engagement with disease, a role analogous to that of paramedical professionals in Western culture, and nurses especially. It seems that other societies have divided healing functions into component parts assigned to two groups: one in which power and authority are dominant and another in which consistence and nurturance are dominant. The suggested link to commonly held features of gender identity is irresistible enough that at the risk of being charged with sexism, we would list some homey but significant facts: children typically have two parents, a mother and father, who differ in the style of their parenting, in their roles within the culture, and in the way they see themselves. If these are acceptable axioms, it seems reasonable to propose that the two dovetailed aspects of the healing function can be thought of as paternal and maternal or as representing features of both parents.

The clothing of medicine men and shamans suggests further hypotheses. In most cases their special costumes include a device, the mask of an animal or a counter-demon, which enhances the wearer's height and enlarges the size of his head. This spectacular healer's garb must encourage the regression that illness is likely to induce of itself. If one recalls the infant's awareness of how small his body is compared with those of adults, it is not unreasonable to conjecture that the medicine man's big head reconstitutes this proportionality. In primitive thought processes, present in sophisticated as well as in so-called primitive peoples, a big head can also signal extraordinary quantities of knowledge. The researches of Spitz (1946) and others have shown that the infant's first recognition of his mother is based upon identification of an area of her face between the tip of the nose and the top of the forehead. The visage that appears to the prone patient, be it of the medicine man, shaman, physician, or nurse, encompasses much the same area of the face and may well have a similar affective cast. Our use of the concept of regression here is not pejorative; indeed the regressed state in illness can be adaptive—a necessary element in healing and recovery.

The medicine man's mask owes part of its effectiveness to the replication of the archaic situation between the caretaking parent and the helpless infant. If the needful patient in any culture feels that he beholds a larger-than-life visage, this may be explained in part by the need to maintain trust in the physician's omniscience. The tandem longings in illness are to be able to regress safely and to yield some portions of autonomy to a dependable, caring figure. Understanding the depth and strength as well as the ontogenetic sources of these longings can produce dramatic improvement in therapeutic effectiveness.

From developmental and cross-cultural evidence it seems reasonable to conclude that a crucial issue for line 3 is the importance of power. Distinctions among those who do the healing seem to relate

to the healer's psychological and physical distance from the patient
and at another level to whether and to what extent power is
achieved by wisdom, physical size, or a potent mixture of both.
Within Western culture, the mythology of medicine is often an
important factor in the decision to enter the profession. And omniscience is always a part of the myth. Some of the heroic doctor figures
who capture children's imagination are fictional, like Sinclair
Lewis's Arrowsmith, or Marcus Welby and Joseph Gannon of later
electronic fame. For those with a different bent, the historical giants
of medicine can be an inspiration: Hippocrates, Vesalius, Osler,
Pasteur, Ehrlich, Bernard. In fiction or biography, doctors conquer
death and illness by power and knowledge. They are rarely, if ever,
depicted as indecisive, although in rare bursts of candor and the
introduction of a racy soupçon of reality, they may be shown struggling with uncertainty. This is fleeting of course, lasting only until
they make the correct and rescuing decision.

Another more urgent precursor related to line 3 and to the attrac-
tion to medicine may occur if the individual himself is ill in childhood, latency, or adolescence, or observes severe illness in those
close to him. At such times the specters of disfigurement, death,
and the agony of uncertainties about the diagnoses are vivid. These
painful experiences are examples of organizing trauma described in
the glossary and discussed in other developmental lines. Understood, and then realistically internalized, they can become well-
placed, paracognitive supports for the edifice of physicianhood.

For us, this suggests that a study of medical students or applicants
to medical school that included information about serious illnesses
in them or in their immediate families might reveal some interesting
data. It would be important not only to collect the facts but to try to
elicit some memories of the concurrent feelings; it would even be
useful to discover how these feelings were dealt with after the immediate crises or losses had passed. These are attitudes, sets, and
values about knowledge and power which can be seen readily in
those on the brink of or engaged in medical training. In fact, they
are so commonplace that they are rarely described in the literature.
The rationale for listing them here is to emphasize that their signifi-

cance relates to the management of knowledge. For example, pre-medical students often seem to have little interest in knowing about matters not relevant to their work. The culturally encouraged competitiveness for admission to medical school certainly emphasizes focused and intense learning. Some doctors remain narrowly concerned with information after graduation and subtly or even openly derogate those who are drawn to a broader scope of knowledge. So it is that physicians render themselves vulnerable to the charge of being antiintellectual. The fact is that most doctors concentrate on knowledge about healing. Of course, in any sample of medical students one can discover those who have extensive background in art, literature, and the general humanities but, especially in recent decades, these individuals are rare.

We hypothesize that for all who confront the counterpoint between knowledge and power, and the longing and need for omnipotence via omniscience, there are two kinds of outcomes. Where omniscience yields the most gratification and there is little or no desire to heal, the result may be a teacher or scholar. In any case the psychological result will be a person gratified by the acquisition of knowledge for its own sake. For those who turn to medicine, a kind of selective, cognitive filter is in operation even in adolescence. This filter depends for its fabric and construction on paracognitive factors with roots in experiences as archaic as those which determine the choice of scholarship. Those who are bound for physicianhood are attracted to the kind of specific knowledge that will add to their ability to manage illness and suffering. For them, knowledge for its own sake is at best a luxury which can be ill afforded; at worst it is extraneous, a distraction from the work of acquiring the volume of information which is the indispensable substance of their learning. The scholar is content to know, and occasionally to enjoy the display of his knowledge; the doctor must know specifically and be able to act promptly upon what he knows. The scholar may be a kind of collector; the doctor, by definition, is an informed doer.

This may explain why, in retrospective studies of scholastic records, doctors are often found to be only average students in grade school. In the more recent past, competition for admission to medical school has become keen, and grade point averages are so large a determining factor that the accumulation of A's has acquired new meaning. Premedical students often strive for high grades in all subjects as early as junior high school and certainly in high school and premedical studies. This may be less because they are truly interested in English literature, advanced Latin, or the music of the Middle Ages than because their goal is an overall grade point average which will increase their chances with admissions committees.

Graduated lines of development such as we have proposed here mean that each succeeding stage becomes increasingly, in fact, exponentially more complex. Later stages like the one under discussion tend to have longer critical periods. For the sake of clarity we want to reiterate and amplify some aspects of the definition of critical stage already given. There is no implication that if maturational progress does not occur during the time range suggested as critical, it is unlikely to happen at all. But we do believe that there are periods during which maturational vectors with genic, cultural, and educational components coincide, making maximal development possible and psychologically most efficient. For instance, there exists a specifiable age span which delineates when a human infant within normal ranges of development usually begins to sit erect with support. The specifications derive from how developmental schema are sequenced and from genetic determinants; careful allowances are made for individual variation. Attempting to specify analogous age ranges for the more complex maturational tasks, such as the achievement of a coherent sense of personal identity, is considerably more difficult. The task is the same, but the number of variables to be considered has vastly increased, and the precision with which the span of developmental appropriateness can be circumscribed decreases.

The critical stage for line 3 extends over a longer period of time than earlier maturational eras, often well past graduation from medical school, and there are correspondingly extended ranges of levels of intensity in the critical stage. Onset of the critical stage may be triggered by the fateful letter which announces acceptance to medical school. There is an enormous impact in the realization that the person is to have a chance to become a doctor, "for real."

During the teaching of the basic sciences, students who may have displayed little interest in these areas in premedical studies (except for the general necessity for keeping the overall grade point average high), may become focused, enlivened in their learning styles. This may be because now they are learning with a purpose—the material is clearly oriented toward their life's work. Medical students sometimes complain bitterly that what they learn in the basic science courses seems irrelevant. At another level, however, they seem to realize, and some can acknowledge, that the information offered them in these years is precisely relevant; that the faculty are right to insist that they master the knowledge basic to the calling within which they have finally achieved apprenticeship. At a psychological level, this learning satisfies the students' desire for the kind of omniscience they hope, and not without reason, will enhance their weaponry for coping with illness and death. It is also appealing (at times) because it is precise and "scientific"; it is knowledge burdened with the minimum of uncertainty. And finally it is hallowed by tradition, an important point in a calling as old as medicine.

There are other, more realistic reasons for learning the basic sciences, a first phase in the critical stage. Students are acutely aware, in the United States at least, that if they do not learn these fields, and well, they will not pass the competency examinations required before they can move on to clinical work. During early medical studies longing for clinical contact comes not only from the wish to end apprenticeship. It is also an expression of the desire to begin at once to merge and express power, touch, control, empathy, and to execute the totality of medical performance. Basic science studies provoke impatience because they force postponement of attempts at such coalescence and possibly premature movement toward maturation. But these studies are also comforting because they are paracognitively appropriate. The delay they impose provides an opportunity for the development of internal support systems which will facilitate absorption and consolidation of knowledge. The internalization and perhaps overlearning of certain varieties of knowledge, crisp, discrete, established, lends confidence to students' feelings that they are accumulating cognitive competence.

This increasing confidence may rekindle ideas of omnipotence like those which were important as the very earliest precursors for physicianhood. These may surface in conscious awareness as feeling states of self-satisfaction, mild euphoria, triumph, and the like. As the earliest infantile omnipotence was tempered but not extinguished by general reality, the rekindling of fantasies and hopes for cognitive omnipotence in early studies will ideally be tempered but not destroyed by clinical experience. These are important issues in the next two developmental lines, the development of a sturdy ego-ideal and a working career identity. Observing students in the first year of medical school one has the impression that they are loading cargo for the trip toward physicianhood. Although the process is backbreaking and lengthy and they long to be off on the journey, the necessity for the chores cannot really be questioned. Educational problems throng when students entertain fantasies that this cargo of knowledge will serve not only for the journey through medical school but for the remainder of their professional careers. Later, to be sure, most realize that although the knowledge garnered during the basic science years is valuable and serves them well, it is only a beginning. To carry the nautical analogy one step further, the information cargo is not static; it can decay, dissipate, or turn to dead weight as it becomes obsolete. As practice continues, review of the basic science knowledge appropriate to each specialty will necessitate periodic stops at appropriate ports for restocking the hold.

If fantasies of omniscience have high points in medical training, the end of the formal basic science training is one of them. Girded with concise, well-ordered knowledge, the student ventures into the clinical arena. But at this juncture illusions of omniscience and omnipotence confront reality, with results beneficial for cognitive and paracognitive development. The student must begin to explore and scan the ranges between certainty and uncertainty, activity and less activity, and the various species of omniscience and corollary omnipotence. The results of these explorations influence the length and intensity with which this developmental phase approaches mastery and consolidation.

In the course of these exploratory ventures the student may journey to the outer ranges represented by many medical specialties. For example, radiologists or surgeons seem to be physicians who have maximized power and omniscience. The specialists themselves may not feel that they have less uncertainty to deal with, but only that increased knowledge makes their decisions more difficult. The fact is that the area of their professional activity has been firmly and more narrowly delineated than in other specialties. And the extent to which a doctor restricts the area of healing he will be responsible for also determines in large measure the amount of uncertainty he must cope with.

For the surgeon, power has been extended and uncertainty diminished in some instances by fortuitous developments in medical technology. Procedures considered extraordinary and dangerous fifty years ago are now routine, carrying a minimum threat to life and maximum hope for a favorable and rapid outcome. Other operations formerly impossible even to consider, for example some of those in cardiac and thoracic surgery, can now be attempted, often with promising results. Some of this progress has been made possible by advances in such allied fields as biomedical engineering. But regardless of the reasons, it is not surprising that, watching the passing parade of specialties and teachers during medical school, the surgeon is conspicuous as the most active, confident, firmly in command, the most direct and forceful in his relation to healing. Surgeons are often the mythic heroes for those—medical students and others—with needs for active physical mastery rather than for conceptual, metaphoric, or symbolic kinds of mastery.

Another specialty where uncertainty seems reduced and omniscience heightened is radiology. The radiologist's especially penetrating perceptual access to the human body is compelling because it is consonant with the archaic curiosity and interest in the body which are among the very earliest precursors of physicianhood. Although radiologists will demur that they deal only with "celluloid and shadows," that is not how students view the situation. Not only can this doctor "see" things which others cannot, but the exactness and diagnostic importance of what he sees and of what he can know from what he sees is impressive. This privileged and very special kind of omniscience is appealing by itself. But in addition, the diagnostic radiologist rarely deals directly with situations in which there is a threat to the life of the patient or in which he is involved in treatment; he provides the data that other physicians use. Thus, his omnipotence, or perhaps one might more properly say the students' fantasies about his omnipotence, are left undisturbed.

At the other end of the range of the student's specialty safari is psychiatry. This often appears as a specialty in which the diseases themselves are the essence of uncertainty. They are intangible and invisible, and the evidence for their existence—illusions, amnesias, or violent, inexplicable outbursts—are frightening. These symptoms can only with difficulty be related to pathological processes. While the doctor who appears to know his way with these invisible diseases and can remain relatively unperturbed by their manifestations may be reluctantly admired, he is more apt to be feared and protectively ridiculed. Many students, tacitly reinforced by faculty, set the entire field and its practitioners outside the realm of medicine because of its apparent uncertainty; psychiatric knowledge is dismissed as mystical mumbo jumbo. It is true that the entities which constitute psychiatric disease are perceived even by recalcitrant students as causing suffering, but often these diseases cannot be entertained as objects of serious interest. The reason lies in the fact that at this stage in development, psychiatric illnesses, in some ways the very essence of uncertainty, pose a difficult, almost insoluble problem. Students who are not yet clear about how they will manage uncertainty as a psychological totality will be too uncomfortable to be able to learn about the seemingly nebulous world of mental illness.

The student must also deal with a universal problem in thinking about the psychoses. Even healthy individuals have thoughts and especially dreams which are mysterious, violent, and inexplicable. Observing psychotics is frightening because it reminds people that there is the dangerous possibility of identifying with them. Psychotic patients often express some of what the student himself has imagined or thought, and the anxiety that this generates adds another impediment to learning. The material of psychiatry is not only strangely vague, it is also naggingly familiar.

The primary-care specialties—family medicine, pediatrics, and internal medicine—occupy a midway position in the spectrum from lesser to greater uncertainty and omnipotence. These fields are less protected than others by narrowing of interest. By definition, their scope is to treat as much of the totality of disease as possible. And, in addition, though some of the biomedical engineering advantages have accrued to these specialties also, the very volume and variety of the morbidity they encompass leaves them more vulnerable to uncertainties and to error.

The whole custom of the Clinico-Pathological-Conference (CPC) is a response to the challenge of uncertainty. It is an occasion for solving the riddle, an opportunity to discover the solution to the "mystery" of a case. Whether the CPC occurs orally as in an individual hospital, or in writing as, for example, in the *New England Journal of Medicine*, the pattern is the same. A case is presented which poses an obscure and difficult problem. Often, to add excitement to the challenge, and to emphasize the importance of coping with uncertainty, crucial information is omitted. A platoon of distinguished faculty or specialists are then invited to comment upon the case equipped only with the incomplete data and, in the absence of having actually seen the patient, they are expected to come to conclusions about the diagnosis and treatment.

One peak in the feeling of omnipotence is at the end of basic science studies. There are at least two others. Achievement of these pinnacles is followed quickly by a descent into sustainable ranges as the feeling of omnipotence is confronted with clinical experience. The drama is frequently enacted again during the senior year. At this point many students seem convinced that an appropriate degree of omnipotence is well within their grasp: They know all they need to know. The beginning of graduate training usually dislodges this conviction, but as the end of specialty training nears, a conviction about omnipotence often reappears, and takes on a slightly more grandiose tone. In the words of one medical educator, "The senior resident really thinks he knows everything worth knowing." Such a situation signals that the paracognitive soil is clearly not ripe for the input of additional knowledge. This is no reason, however, for educational efforts to be abandoned or slackened. On the contrary, such points are often an optimal place at which to intercept the notion of omniscience by introducing the learner to clinical dilemmas, puzzles, mysteries. If all else fails, he may profit from a glimpse of the consequences of possible catastrophes. The valleys of self-esteem in training, where the feeling of sufficient omniscience may be shaky, can also be put to good use: Cognitive material can often be absorbed more readily to allay anxiety and reinstate confidence. There is an important distinction between confidence and grandiosity, between believing that one's knowledge is adequate but never complete and feeling that it is equal to anything. The master-teacher, especially in the clinical fields, must be alert to the growing ascendance of and the manner in which omnipotence and omniscience are being paracognitively managed. Only in this way can he offer promptly the appropriate antidotes for both problems.

We have mentioned some of the techniques that can be employed when omniscience reaches toxic if affectively pleasant levels. There are also methods that will aid the student or resident plagued with a related difficulty, the feeling that he knows nothing, or will never know enough. In these situations encouragement and support as well as additional information and supervised experience can often restore proper balance. In most cases these conventional instructional devices will suffice to deal with the problems. If difficulty persists, however, there is the possibility that personal psychopathology may be extensive enough to deform paracognitive support structures and significantly and perhaps permanently impair their functioning. Here clearly, prompt assessment of the extent of the psychopathology and the amount of incapacitation is essential.

It may well be that coalescence and mastery in this line occur only in the crucible of practice, when ultimate responsibility rests upon the physician and there are no teachers or institutions to buffer the effect of triumph or error, when caution, humility, and growing self-acceptance often displace ideas of omnipotence. To use a chemical analogy it is as though each of the elements needed to form a new compound were added throughout the critical phase. At the same time, work conditions increasingly approximate those which will lead to synthesis. The final step for many physicians may only be possible as they enter medical work as full professionals, accountable to their patients, their peers, and in a sense the whole society. The toleration for uncertainty is something that must be taught and learned throughout a lifetime in medicine. Mastery of this peculiarly unpleasant stress probably reaches asymptomatic levels only after some years and not for all physicians. For those who teach doctors, constant reminders of the need to be aware of uncertainty and to possess reasonable safeguards through which it can be managed both for the patients' and the doctors' benefit are not amiss at anytime.

In this line of development, perhaps more than in any others, adequate teaching and learning hinge upon astute, incessant, and accurate monitoring of the paracognitive apparatus of the learner as he progresses via a number of swings and returns toward comfortable and appropriate management of the wishes for omniscience, omnipotence, and the capacity to live with and work in spite of uncertainty. Figure 5 is a graphic depiction of the points we have discussed, and shows the condition of the learners to be described in the vignettes below, Student J and Dr. K.

Student J, in the first months of his junior year, was considered one of the brightest students in his class. He had previously treated the patient, a man in his sixties with heart disease including auricular fibrillation. When the man returned for a checkup, a routine EKG recording was taken, the student glanced at it briefly and ordered an exercise stress test. If a preceptor had not intervened there might have been serious danger to the patient's health and life, for Student J was experiencing a premature peaking of omniscience, at the beginning of the third rather than the fourth year of training. He felt that his inspection of the tracing had been sufficient to reach the conclusion that there were no contraindications to the exercise stress test. From a teaching standpoint the student exhibited an even graver symptom. When, at the preceptor's suggestion,

FIGURE 5

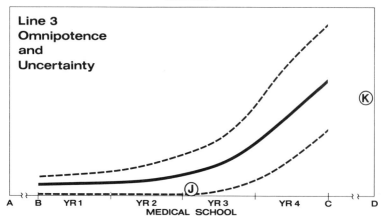

the EKG rhythm strip was reexamined, he could not recognize that it was in any way pathological, in spite of the clear absence of the P waves indicating continuing fibrillation, information Student J was expected to have learned thoroughly at this stage in his cognitive progress. Realizing that he had not, the preceptor reviewed the characteristics of EKG patterns and emphasized the possible hazards of ordering an exercise test for patients with the findings just displayed. Interestingly enough, Student J's sense of being in the right, of really "knowing what he was doing" in this case seemed unshaken. The preceptor was palpably distressed. He was convinced that Student J would not review his cardiology as had been suggested and as he plainly needed to. Worse still, the teacher was left with the feeling that if a similar situation arose in the future, the student would still order the test.

Dr. K. was a very bright physician in his mid thirties, who had completed three years of residency in internal medicine and a year and a half of practice. Within the span of forty-eight hours, two of his patients in a primary-care setting died. As far as anyone could tell, he was in no way responsible for the deaths; the course of the diseases was puzzling and their etiology uncertain even after autopsy. The deaths had been sudden and unexpected. Even after an agonizingly thorough review with peers of the charts, the lab findings, and the clinical material, the young physician remained badly shaken. Seeking out a trusted older colleague, he voiced with great despair his most vexing doubt: "Do you suppose that after all I wasn't cut out to be a doctor?"

These two vignettes illustrate stages in the management of omniscience and omnipotence which are less than optimal. The condition of Student J seems the most malignant, because in his case the conviction of omniscience resulted in blocking adequate perception. Such perceptual obstacles constitute one of the most substantial impediments to teaching, and until they can be cleared, eventual mastery must be considered at risk.

In the episode about Dr. K there seems more reason for optimism. After talking with the senior colleague about how much he wished never to make a mistake and having received genuine and appropriate support from his peers, the internist recovered his composure. Even more promising were comments which led his colleagues to believe that in the future the needs to be omniscient and omnipotent might be modulated and eventually managed comfortably.

Lines 1, 2, and 3 have been disentangled to clarify their presentation. Actually, they are elastic as well as interwoven. The next two lines of paracognitive development are of a different order of magnitude, more melds than combinations. They emerged from efforts to use elements from the first three lines and additional data about physicianhood to construct better explanatory frameworks. If they are more intricate, it is because they are an attempt to be more integrative.

CHAPTER 6

Developmental Line 4:
The Formation of
the Physician Ego-Ideal

The final two lines map the growth of structures which are more complex than those of the first three lines. Each of the last two is a strand, but also, separately and together, they form matrices, the warp and woof within which the fabric and pattern of physicianhood can begin to take shape. Like the preceding ones, these paracognitive supports, if adequately developed, facilitate the acquisition of clinical skills and the mastery of knowledge. In particular, they contribute to the ease and smooth efficiency of interpersonal relationships with patients and colleagues. Progress in the emergence of these structures is not so open to observation as are manifestations of the earlier lines, nor is it so easily tracked. Like most late growth phenomena, they are apt to come into view slowly, giving only intermittent clues about progress to both the learner and those who must assess his potential.

For most people the ego-ideal is that idea of the inner self which is comprised of standards and imperatives about the kind of person he or she must be to be comfortable. The ego-ideal also provides the substrate for what the individual must attempt to *become* in order to remain internally satisfied and to feel socially valued. In sum, the term *ego-ideal* as used here encompasses the definitions for each individual's needs for perfectibility. Erickson has written a poetic expression of this state of being: "In the evaluation of the dominant moods of any historical period, it is important to hold fast to the fact that there are always islands of self-sufficient order—on farms and castles, in homes, studies and cloisters—where sensible people manage to live relatively lusty and decent lives: as moral as they must be, as free as they may be, and as masterly as they can be. If we only knew it, this elusive arrangement is happiness" (*Young Man Luther*, 1958, p. 75). To be sure, in this statement Erikson expresses his fantasy of a personal as well as a societal ego-ideal. But he is also depicting any individual's wishes for an optimally tranquil balance between reality, both internal and external, and the longing to transcend the limits of such realities.

To be more precise, we need to expand and elaborate the definition given in the glossary. The ego-ideal has its roots in a stage of early infancy where neither the distinction between the self and the environment nor the demands of external reality are recognized. The meaning of this stage for line 1 was reviewed in chapter 3 as it related to the management of objectivity and empathy and again in the consideration of line 3 as a factor in the internal struggles for a balance between reality and omnipotence and omniscience. This first phase is known technically as the presymbiotic (autistic) stage in the sense that there is not yet any recognition of the individual as a separate organism. This phenomenon has been described at length by Mahler (1968) and confirmed by a number of researchers in human development.

In adults there is no memory of these early experiences, but echoes and reminiscences of them appear in the themes of myths, in religion (as in ideas of reunion and heavenly bliss), and at times and in some persons in regressive tendencies to indulge in primitive pleasures such as alcohol, eating, massages, bathing, sleeping, or mind-altering drugs. Fantasies and memories of blissful union of self and world are the ontogenetic archeological artifacts out of which, much later, the ego-ideal is formed. The process, briefly, is as follows.

The normal infant gradually learns to discern, in addition to displeasure and contentment, the existence of an entity, usually a parent, who is intimately related to these states and to changes in them—the symbiotic phase.[1] The relationship of the infant to his symbiotically functioning adults is literally vital. They serve as in-

---

1. There has since birth been a symbiosis in the sense of biological support, but the symbiotic phase appears when the infant makes the distinction between self and other.

tervening forces, manipulating the environment at a time when the infant is highly vulnerable and helpless to do so himself. The environmental manipulators, or significant others as they are sometimes called, are sensed and often utilized as an extension of the infant's wish to manage everything, a vehicle for maintaining infantile omnipotence vicariously.

Discrepancies between the infant's desires and the decisions of those who care for him inevitably arise, and as they do, a beginning outline of reality takes shape within the child. This involves loss of some of the feelings of inviolable power and importance (narcissism), but in most cases the losses are not so painful that they cannot be sustained, accepted, and eventually internalized. Thus modified, they form a new and more adaptive sense of self whose potency is tested as the child experiments in dealing with the outside world on his own.

This next phase has been called one of rapprochement (Mahler 1968), because independent attempts at negotiating with the outside alternate with frequent returns to caretakers. A toddler exploring a new room is a good example of the prototypical behavior of this phase. His expeditions to outer perimeters are regularly interspersed with returns to (usually) his mother's person; at a later stage, visual rather than tactile contact will be employed to make sure that she is still there; later still, contact will be less frequent, more for testing of reality than out of a need to assure the presence of a psychological base. Such practicing, often designated as a separate phase, results in further modification of the child's ideas about his importance, influence, and potential for modifying the world to comply with his desires and needs. The type and style of the later ego-ideal are partly determined at this stage. If the relatedness to nurturing persons is positive, reinforcing, growth promoting, it will be easier for the child to internalize these tendencies as nuclei from which to generate his own structures for carrying on a responsible (and happy) life. The importance of the process is not only that experiences with parenting figures are internalized, but that these internalizations form the bases for later structures in the child's (and eventually the adult's) personality.

The next stage in the sequence has been called the separation-individuation phase. When the child becomes sufficiently sure of who he is, of what he can do or cause to have done for him, and when he is confident in his knowledge of the environment, he can be comfortably separated from intermediaries for longer and increasingly stable periods of time. With this achievement comes the possibility of even more expansive projects such as for example, entrance into nursery school. For our discussion, the most important point is that in this process of separating and becoming a free-standing individual, the child internalizes and uses elements and operations from earlier experiences. The sense of self moves from being a nearly total function in the symbiotic phase to a state where it constitutes a monitor, a guide for behavior. Being on good terms with one's self (one's ego-ideal) corresponds closely with Erikson's earlier quoted description of happiness. (There are many ways in which aspects of external reality become active parts of the personality. We have used *internalization* as a general term that includes all of them, reserving the task of differentiation to a later date.) The result of such internalizations is often expressed by the common observation that we deal with others much in the way we were dealt with. But matters are not quite so simple. We also deal with others much in the way we wish we were dealt with. To summarize, and return to the ego-ideal, the internal parameters that determine what each individual needs in order to feel satisfied with himself and what he will need to do to remain satisfied with himself (perfectibility) will have emerged out of the early struggles and experiences with closeness and independence.

Later aspects of the unfolding process are superimposed upon and intermingled with early precursors of the ego-ideal and contribute to its eventual mode and function. Among these later happenings are the societal demands that are imposed on children between the ages of two and five by parental figures. In past years these requirements were thought of by psychologists mainly in terms of controls, such as those involved in toilet training and tidiness in general. But plainly our society also demands that children learn early to rein in other, more complex and primitive forces, capable of many subtleties of expression. Children are expected to cope in acceptable ways with hostility and wishes for closeness or exclusive possession of loved figures.

Achievement of these controls is optimally induced through loving identification with parenting figures. The enterprise is given added impetus by shame. An example that illustrates both identificatory and shaming complexities is bladder regulation, a function which is linked with the genitals and with dependent and loving, as well as angry, feelings for the mother. In establishing this control, identification with the mother is especially important; if the identification is robust it will support smoothly functioning development of bladder control, and shame and anger will be kept at manageable levels. If identification with the mother is frail or conflicted, there are usually detours or failure; shame and anger can become serious problems. The success with which the compliance is accomplished determines the extent and tone of feelings about continuing nurturance, and as we have emphasized, components of personality related to nurturance are often important in the choice of physicianhood as a calling. Additionally, a mixture of succoring and controlling needs persist as derivatives in most aspects of medical work.

Another example of regulation is bowel function. Control of this bodily function is seldom accomplished without generating some hostility and aggression and is usually motivated by shame, by invoking disgust, and often by establishing a link to morality. These factors—shame, disgust, morality—also relate to doctoring, especially when they can be seen in the doctor's (and medical student's) sense of responsibility to patients, colleagues, and institutions and his commitment to a demanding profession.

The fact that a child has become toilet trained or has learned not to bite or kick others does not indicate the establishment of a structure within the personality. It is evidence of the taming or redirection of forces that lead to adaptation, subsequently to structure, and then to structure of a particular type. The styles of these adaptations do not usually become well settled in the personality until the child is from three to six years old.

These working hypotheses, which have served well as a

framework for understanding general growth, can help to explain the special features of the physician ego-ideal. One of the stable phenomena of physicianhood is the remarkable intensity with which doctors relate to their practice. This relatedness is often acknowledged as connected to the doctor's sense of worth, an important part of his sense of self, and thus a large life force. It is in this arena that the questions will be decided about how good a doctor he must be and how good a doctor he must strive to become in order to remain relatively free of conflict.

Successful adaptations in early developmental stages mean that mastery and control are achieved with components of both pleasure and stress. When mastery without significant conflict is accomplished with the help of gentle and empathic parenting figures, these events will create complex links which loop back to the first three lines of development. Consider, for example, line 1. Suppose that a child has been guided through the tasks of achieving societally demanded controls by people whose behavior leads him to sense that they appreciate and have attempted to understand his feelings of fury, of frustration, of strenuous effort, and of triumph. Such a child, as he matures, will find that he can mirror and may seek to duplicate these capacities in his dealings with a wide spectrum of significant others. With such early experiences as a backdrop, many callings for which empathy is necessary are likely to be appealing and accessible to the individual—medicine among them.

If his mastery of earlier controls of bodily and societal functions has been accomplished by gentle encouragement, flexibility, and tolerance, the child will have added motivation to deal in a nurturant fashion (line 2) with those he encounters as he matures. He may, in fact seek to outdo the nurturance he experienced, an especially important transformation for those who will subsequently become physicians. The particular manner of this transformation will be specified by the qualities of the ego-ideal: How lenient or demanding is the person in his standards for himself? Do the approaches to these standards sponsor progress or regression? Do they emphasize shame or encourage disregarding it? Whatever the answers, the internal reworking of nurturance-received to nurturance-performed will yield inner comfort and gratification in differing styles, and for the physician-to-be it will support work which usually results in rewards from a grateful environmental gestalt—parents, peers, teachers, and ultimately patients.

Clearly, secure mastery of bodily functions, affects, and the other psychic complexities that we have described enhance the young child's feeling of omnipotence (line 3). This is quite different from the infantile omnipotence of the early months of life because it emerges from the kind of adaptive encounter with reality which physicians (as most everyone else) will confront again and again during training and, in fact, as long as professional work continues. This species of omnipotence, tempered by reality and uncertainty, can be a giant developmental step forward.

The material on the precursors of the physician ego-ideal has been lengthier than for any of the preceding phases, and with good reason. We must now examine how its formation differs as a developmental construct from the three lines already discussed. We have postulated that the three earlier stages of development of the physician's paracognitive apparatus show maximum acceleration during medical school. The events that can be observed during this period provide support for this proposition. For example, during the period of societal demands, the toddler will have faced anxiety about whether or not mastery is possible, the frightening contingency that he may fail. Medical students are perennially subject to the same kind of anxiety. When and as mastery has been possible in the childhood phase of development, it will usually have included joy and confidence at having surmounted not only the adaptation, but the anxiety that accompanied it. The same sequence can be observed in the relief and the increasing confidence (and coincidentally the slowly growing sense of self which includes physicianhood) which occur as medical students surmount successive *rites de passage* in their training.

Another result of successful mastery of societal and bodily controls may be the strengthening of healthy components related to ambition. The style in which these trends are expressed will depend upon the ways in which the child's identification with parenting figures developed. As a toddler masters a bodily function connected with the genitals, or an affective function such as aggression, he or she may well imagine expanding the scope of this mastery. Future life-styles will be much influenced by whether such imaginings are snuffed out, allowed freedom of expression, encouraged reasonably or with urgency. Such events can lead to ambition in fields other than medicine. It is the junction of the developments related to control, mastery, and ambition with the parallel and overlapping growth in empathy, objectivity, nurturance, and omnipotence which is unique to physicians and contributes to the structure of the physician ego-ideal.

Among doctors, differing ego-ideals produce remarkable variation in the form ambition takes. It can lead to a wish to practice the most excellent kind of medicine, to provide the best possible care for one's patients, a bonding with the nurturant line of development. Less successfully resolved, it can generate a driven competitiveness which leaves the doctor unable to be satisfied with his achievements, whether in practice, teaching, or administration. For such persons there are always new worlds to conquer; they suffer a kind of frustrated grandiosity. This turn of affairs is bonded with less healthy aspects of line 3: There is a less than optimal resolution of the desire for omniscience and omnipotence and instead a preoccupation with them, resulting in stunted development in the areas of nurturance and empathy.

We have stressed that interwoven aspects from the earlier three lines of development are specific to the physician ego-ideal. To sharpen the concept and inveigh against reification, there are two final points specifying boundaries, i.e., what the physician ego-ideal is *not*.

First, the physician ego-ideal does not encompass a polarity as have the preceding lines of development. It is a structure or form of organization within the personality which relates to other functional segments of the personality. The extent of synergism and potentiation among these areas will determine what kinds of problems can be expected at the various levels of development toward physician-hood and how serious they will be. Many forces within and without organized medicine are concerned with difficulties in producing adequate selection procedures for admission to medical school. In other studies (1968, 1970) we observed that disequilibrium among the components of the personality of practicing physicians led to disequilibrium with the practice. Often this brought the doctor to training programs; depending upon the severity of the disequilibrium, it might also bring him to treatment.

Second, the ego-ideal is not merely a receptacle of qualities and traits; rather it is one part of an organically functioning personality and as such has characteristics unique to it as a whole. These characteristics—transformations of earlier experiences and identifications—become so distinctive as to permit the physician relatively unconflicted pursuit of his life's work. Like all of us, the physician needs an ego-ideal which is occupationally suitable. What we shall be describing in the material to follow is the growth, style, and topography of these kinds of ego-ideals.

In the beginning of this chapter we described at some length the different orders of complexities inherent in lines 4 and 5. These lines are in some ways better thought of as phases, in contrast to the first three developmental lines, which are developmental stages. Line 4 is a kind of mathematical derivative, a sum and product of the preceding three. It begins in the hubbub of medical school, but its critical period has more variance in every aspect than its predecessors had.

The earliest beginnings of the physician ego-ideal occur as nurturant drives are gradually transformed and transferred to the idea of the healing process. A reprise of this transformation might be as follows: In the early years of human psychic life there emerges first self-awareness and at much the same time an absorption with the self which is often called self-love. Eventually there is a reversal, so that nurturant persons are also loved and later identified with. Out of the elements of all these phases and in particular those elements from identification with loved figures, the structure of the ego-ideal is formed. These events have special significance if medicine is one of the vocational fantasies of the preschool years. If the fantasy persists and becomes a goal, the transformed drives are attached to the body and person of others—patients-to-be, or imaginary patients like pets, younger siblings, disabled or disadvantaged peers. The unconscious rehearsals with these substitutes are an important force in structuring the nascent physician ego-ideal. Such practicing also indicates that foundations for the next steps are underway. The physician ego-ideal builds on the earlier sequences listed above and makes use of the feeling of shame as a powerful motivational source.

By the time medical training begins, the physician ego-ideal may be well on its way to becoming a firmly established and comfortable part of the personality. Freshmen medical students are second to none in their therapeutic fervor, but this fervor is restrained at first. Though for generations students have chafed at such restraints, it may be that the delay provides a needed moratorium during which there can be preparation for the transition from the yearning to be nurturant to healing as a professional act. In any case, manifest empirical evidence about the onset of the critical stages of the development of the physician ego-ideal cannot be observed until the internal structure is allowed to become operative: when the student begins to spend substantial amounts of time doing clinical work. The uneasiness which most students feel at the start of this work stems from their awareness at varying degrees and levels that the physician ego-ideal is not yet quite steady. The shakiness is related to the stage of completion of the metamorphosis from genetic ego-ideal, to beginning physician ego-ideal, and finally, to firmly operational physician ego-ideal. The stakes are high, for much shame attaches to failure to assess the level of development and do the work.

As in all developmental crises, the anxiety the student feels may not be objectively related exclusively to cognitive problems but to a tendency to regress in the face of the assumption of the new and more advanced functions faced at a transition zone. At such moments students frequently seize upon the standards (the physician ego-ideals) of their teachers as a kind of prosthesis. The speed and degree with which these can be relinquished is one good indicator of the variety of development which will occur. Most students first begin intermittently to function autonomously and gradually take over more and more of the work. The process picks up momentum as the student's physician ego-ideal locks onto his trans-actions with patients as a means of expressing within the profes-sional sphere not only mastery of nurturance, but recognition of omnipotence, tolerance for uncertainty, and a capacity to oscillate between objectivity and empathy.

Part of the increased mastery is accomplished by differentiation, the evolution of varied styles with which to accomplish healing. Distinctive modes emerge for diagnostic work, for acute and chronic situations, for instances where steady support is needed, and many more. This epigenesis is another signal of advancing maturity. Learn-ers cannot modulate or vary the performance of any task until its basic requirements have been comfortably overlearned.

As for the termination of the critical period, what occurs is pre-dictable for a developmental era founded on mastery of early phases and the capacity to synthesize these elements of partial mastery into a new level: There is no time at which we can say that most learners have achieved mastery. Within the acceptable ranges of physician performance there is perpetual examination, revision, and en-hancement of the ego-ideal. However, we can hazard some esti-mates about the time points which mark significant changes in ac-celeration in the process. The public declaration of interest for a given specialty is one such point. It sets the boundaries of the area of knowledge the young doctor will attempt to encompass. Perhaps more important for growth is that in the same choice he decides what shall be excluded as a major concern.

At the beginning of specialty training, transient regressive phenomena are common. Exploration of the new area encourages, indeed demands, internal regrouping, and established balances waver as certain equilibria, especially those concerning omniscience, are jarred. The neophyte realizes keenly and again how little he knows, how meager his healing is, and how vulnerable are his ob-jectivity and ability to feel with the patient. As always, individuals react variably to the newest episode in this developmental scenario. Some feel the need for more skill, knowledge, and responsibility as a heavy burden, others enjoy the challenge, and still others protect themselves with the kind of defensive cynicism spoken of earlier.

Whatever the method of coping with it, the newest confrontation with substantive if familiar narcissistic blows often leads to retrenchment or regression, perhaps in the service of the ego-ideal. Learning by identification often reappears briefly, accompanied by ambivalence about whether to behave as an independent learner or model oneself on another.

Those familiar with residents in any specialty know how fiercely determined they are upon professional independence. Though most can appreciate at a rational level that some supervision is necessary, it is felt as infuriating, and the success of preceptors at this point in medical education may rest on their ability to attend to safeguards for the patient and the institution and at the same time respect the resident's need to "learn by himself." This is a phrase which we translate psychologically to mean, "learn about himself," especially about the kind of physician ego-ideal which will be compatible with his ideals about medicine—now already defined more precisely and thus easier to cope with—and with his own personal growth.

As practice begins and formal training diminishes, the ego-ideal becomes sturdier and more settled. One period of maximum change is usually at an end. If a physician makes a major shift after a long period in practice, a change of specialty or arena of work—from private to hospital practice or from private practice to research or academic medicine—the ego-ideal is involved, of course, but mainly as an aspect of a crisis of identity and is thus most relevant for discussion in line 5.

The completeness and style achieved in line 4 will be determined, as in the preceding lines, by how synthetic and integrative the learning has been, and to what extent this advanced kind of learning has been interdigitated with the developing personality of the physician. Simultaneous, global personal development serves as a set of regulatory boundaries (or parameters) encompassing the growing physician ego-ideal and also accommodating functions and structures related to extraprofessional life.

The hypotheses we have advanced are limited to the professional sphere; attempts to apply them to other areas of physicians' operations or to other varieties of learning must be approached with caution and an investigative attitude. In spite of the allure of such an adventure, the dangers inherent in extrapolation are analagous to errors which occur when there is an attempt to transpose the physician ego-ideal into alien surroundings. A commonplace example of such extrapolations and their risks are the medical and psychic consequences when physicians care for their own families. The following example illustrates the boundary conditions for the physician ego-ideal and the ranges of its workable limits.

Illnesses like mild pharyngitis or minor digestive problems are handled comfortably by most physicians when these conditions occur in members of their own families. Although the physician ego-ideal is not operating in a doctor-patient relationship in the customary sense, the transaction can usually be managed. There are other instances, however, which are clearly beyond the pale. One cluster of such perturbing instances which is frequently observed is the unpleasant yet inescapable bind that occurs when terminally or urgently ill patients demand to be looked after by doctors who are close to them. Like most of those who have studied physicians, we have witnessed the suffering and distortion of function which results. The doctor's objectivity becomes vulnerable as the empathic pull becomes too strong for adequate management. The executive component of nurturance may falter, and even knowledge which has been well integrated and thoroughly overlearned can become unretrievable.

In a less grim vein, few physicians have not had excellent advice rudely thrown out of court by spouse or children, only to have the same counsel accepted and complied with when it came from a colleague. The grounds for dismissal are usually stated as: "What do you know?" We suspect the translation is, "Though valued, you are not the doctor here." And a possible inframessage is: "You are needed as parent (or spouse or sibling) and cannot be spared to be doctor."

The extent to which the physician ego-ideal has become comfortably embedded in the matrix of the personality will determine the comfort and aplomb with which such pulls and tugs are managed and will provide one kind of evidence of the completeness and style of mastery. Relinquishment of the doctoring function in the "What-do-you-know?" case brings relief in the form of lifted responsibility. This renunciation is sanctioned, even encouraged, by one of medicine's oldest ethical statements and by virtue of the patient's rejection. Where close life figures plead for care out of fear and desperation, the physician ego-ideal and the personality are more severely tested.

Another example of the boundaries and interfacing of the ego-ideal in the total personality of the physician can be observed as physicians function in groups whose goals are not truly tied to the calling, as in medical politics or exercises in continuing medical education. Restraints and prohibitions essential to healing are often suspended in these milieux because they encumber; tribal emnities and territorial feuds are no less common than in any other human group. Conversely, where doctors operate in groups which support their work, the functions of the physician ego-ideal are potentiated. To understand what venerable and powerful ties yoke physicians together, one need only recall that the Aesculapians were a brotherhood whose initiation rites included oaths of allegiance to each other as well as to Apollo and to curing. The dread of loss of respect and acceptance by peers is still an especially fateful issue for physicians.

There is a parallel phenomenon: Accepting and faithful patients usually elicit the best medical care. Their beliefs strengthen and enhance the doctor's ego-ideal by reaffirming the adequacy of his omniscience, thus also fulfilling his altogether understandable requirements for narcissistic gratification. The suspicious or untrusting patient will, via the same route pursued in reverse direction, cause static and interference in doctor-patient communications and delay or even lead to only marginal success in the establishment of a working doctor-patient dyad.

Both extremes in the ways in which doctors function in groups can be illuminating. The "loner" physician, who exists largely apart from the collegial community, must indeed be intrapsychically robust. If he is actually a maverick, he may need to be like Gerald Green's "last angry man," for physicians as a group will respond with ostra-

cism or worse: "That bird is not honest who fouleth his own nest."
At the other end of the continuum the megagroup practices now
proliferating in this country can be viewed as a protective response
to an increasingly informed public which demands the privilege of
questioning, and suspects the doctor who will not or cannot give
satisfactory "answers." Sometimes the request for answers means
explanations, a wish to be included in the doctor's sphere of special
and often mythically conceived knowledge; sometimes it means a
wish to share in decision making. Both of these are consistent with
the educational aspects of healing. At other times, the demand for
"answers" may be a plea for certainty when it cannot honestly be
vouchsafed to the patient, or for favorable news when there is none,
or for instantaneous cure when that is not possible.

Doctors have always had to deal with these kinds of patient needs;
in current practice situations the ability to understand these needs
has become crucial. Intraprofession evolutions are reflected in current medical sociology. The increasing publicity about malpractice
suits and their consequences should not distract us from the realization that conditions are rapidly changing. Malpractice actions are
only one derivative of the interaction between the internal
panoramas in the training and development of physicians that we
have been describing and the escalating magnitude of change in the
social climate of medicine. The physician ego-ideal, the result of
advanced personal and professional development and evolution, can
lead to complicated and highly effective functioning. But it is also a
delicate, vulnerable structure which needs continuing support. External group supports are needed up to and through the formation of
the physician identity; and even later, social pressures that menace
the physician identity must be considered seriously. It follows logi-
cally, perhaps inevitably, that doctors have responded to these new
and unexpected challenges to their omniscience and to suspicions
about their dedication by strengthening the bastions of peer support. Banding together provides needed legal, fiscal, and most importantly, personal safeguards; and these have societal benefits as
well. In the area of peer review, for example, it is doubtful that any

outside critic could be as informed or as demanding as a fellow physician, provided that both parties to the contract, the reviewer and the reviewed, are vouchsafed the ancient guarantees of the calling. Privacy, i.e., the exclusion of outsiders, is the most important.

One indication that the physician ego-ideal is established enough for building upon will sound familiar to those accustomed to a developmental mind set. Where maturation of a function and structure has advanced so that both have achieved separate status, distinct from the whole, they can then become thoroughly internalized and go on to become automatized. As a result, new responses will be available to meet changing conditions adequately. In this context the term *automatized* does not mean "automatic." It is used in Glauber's (1968) sense, for example, to refer to tasks whose regulation usually requires only minimal amounts of mental energy, attention, and time. Where necessary, tasks so mastered can be adapted, the adaptations evaluated, reworked, and gradually installed as new features in the response repertoire. This will be true whether the adaptational demands come from (1) external sources, as in the medical sociological developments we have been discussing; (2) interpersonal sources, such as dealing with ever wider varieties of patient personalities and illnesses; or (3) intrapsychic sources, like coping with an increasing range of professional situations and acquiring the capacity for more refined professional perceptions and skills. This kind of ultimate mastery can be approached as the inner core, the physician ego-ideal, becomes fully grown, intact, and resilient.

Another site for observation of mastery in the functioning of the physician ego-ideal is one routine circumstance in which such functioning must be relinquished: patterns of consultation. This particular behavior of doctors has been studied by medical sociologists (Bynder 1965) and psychiatrists (Fitch 1964), but we can use the investigative data and instances readily observable in any medical setting. Many doctors cling to a difficult patient situation, struggling to manage it, well after a consultant should have been contacted. An overly commanding physician ego-ideal may be one explanation for this. At the other extreme is "the dumping syndrome."[2] We observed one doctor who exemplified this kind of rigidity in the firmness with which he dealt with suicidal ideation. "If a patient even mentions suicide, I send him to a psychiatrist at once. That's dangerous business." Clearly, for this man, the physician ego-ideal had incorporated a hair-trigger alarm system designed to protect doctor and patient. "Dangerous business" referred to the intensity of the doctor's discomfort with intangible threats to life. His inflexible referral custom reflected the freedom to halt promptly his responsibility for the patient's care without feeling ashamed.

Before proceeding to specific documentation we must mention one final site at which to assess mastery in this phase: the doctor's relatedness to his practice. Obviously the driven bonding so often apparent must be the result of some functional hypertrophy of the structure we have hypothesized. Because it relates to other equilibria in the personality, the extent and style of mastery will be determined by how these relationships (between the physician ego-ideal and other personality functions) mesh or slip or miss entirely. Exactly as in other complicated natural arrangements, where there is synergism between the functions or subsystems, fluctuating balances with good stress tolerance will result. If it is needed, evidence for this point can be seen in the increasing number of young physicians (many the sons and daughters of physicians) who are emphatic in their determination to be good parents as well as good doctors, to be intelligent citizens as well as up-to-date professionals, and to be culturally as well as medically astute. The validity of this trend is confirmed by the recent authorization for construction of a new medical school admissions test and by the number of medical schools now weighing broad educational interests and talents as heavily as those pertaining to quantitative and scientific fields.

The following statements may serve as a summary of this section. (1) The physician ego-ideal evolves for use in the work of medicine, but its development depends on networks that involve total personality. (2) Evidence for the state of progress can be found in the ease

---

2. W. F. Sheeley 1962: personal communication.

and accuracy of judgment which determine when medical responsibility can be shouldered and relinquished. The way in which the doctor copes with requests for care of family and close friends and his use of consultants are developmental indicators of this. (3) The capacity to use peer groups as support when needed in dealing with patients, social stresses, and other extramedical pressures is another measure of progress. (4) For us, the most revealing sign of secure formation of the physician ego-ideal, and the one least often accepted as evidence, is the doctor's relatedness to his practice. It is essential to distinguish between commitment and dedication employed principally for healing and the same forces used mainly for personal solace. Devotion to medicine which has its major roots in unconscious needs for self-enhancement, compensatory narcissism, or the need to distract from inner conflicts is a poor sign. It indicates that the clear delineation of this function from the personality as a whole—the prerequisite for automatization—has failed to occur. The best physicians are those who observe most widely and most candidly and whose attention is most strongly held by the body and person of another. Medical training provides an opportunity to develop perceptual-search and cognitively integrated skills in the doctor. The role of the physician ego-ideal is to provide an internal mechanism which enables these skills to attach securely to illness behavior.

Up to this point we have kept to descriptions of the observable and the manifest because the conceptual propositions advanced here are apt to disappear in confusion and obscurity if not grounded in data. Yet if the material remains only at manifest, familiar, and verifiable levels, it may also be liable to the charge of being unremarkable, obvious, or even boring. It would be a kind of irresponsible superficiality to leave the topic without mentioning some of the deeper, if more speculative realms of knowledge intrinsic to this discussion.

The first-level affective imperatives of the physician ego-ideal form a continuum from shame through triumph, from an uneasy sense of inadequacy to a gratifying sense of mastery. Beneath these are connections to the oedipal triangulation and to primary and secondary narcissism. And there are still more primitive and wider ranging affective systems which may be mobilized: helplessness, omnipotence, identification, distancing either by disgust or objectivity. The attachment or "locking on" to illness may be accomplished by combinations of these factors acting in concert with the widely touted "human" capacity to accumulate knowledge and perceptions and delay closure until a whole—a gestalt—of sufficient power congeals. Training for the ability to delay is what is built into basic science and apprenticeship in medicine. Intermingled with developmental processes which are necessary but not sufficient conditions for cognitive absorption, the training energizes the forces described above and gives the contours of the physician ego-ideal.

Figure 6 shows the shape of this line of development and its ranges of variability. In view of our previous statements, it is logical that the best time to gather evidence for progress in this dimension would be during the postgraduate years of medical training. The results of the development would constitute the most precise gauge of its course. But we can identify pieces of evidence, signs, during the undergraduate years. These serve the same purpose as their analogues in medicine: They suggest some of the final results and

FIGURE 6

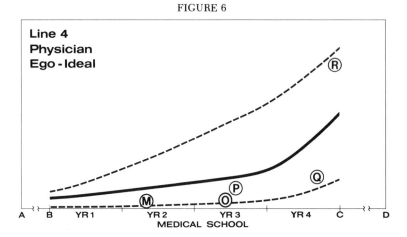

can, with appropriate caution, be taken as guides for educational action.

For proper illustration of this line we needed a graduated set of five examples, each portraying a medical student whose ego-ideal was at a different stage of maturation, as shown in figure 6. The examples range from serious, if not terminal, failure to thrive, at one extreme, to buoyant advance, at the other. Admittedly, there is an imbalance in these vignettes on the side of educational trouble. This is because such situations are the most serious in terms of institutional and personal waste; because they are most in need of accurate, prompt detection and remedial action; and because pathology is easier to understand than success.

1. A Precarious Ego-Ideal

Student M's condition led several faculty members to judge him psychiatrically ill and probably untreatable as early as the middle of his second year in medical school. Performing adequately, but not well, on written tests of cognitive learning, he was barely able to master a portion of required psychomotor and perceptual skills. Most important, these deficits were, by the testimony of all observers, clearly the result of a profound personality disturbance. Self-absorbed and detached, the student seemed unrelated to the task at hand in a way that suggested much psychic distress, encapsulated in a closed internal system. A series, indeed, a veritable platoon of faculty, tried each in a different way to penetrate the barrier. Student M's responses ranged from angry rebuffs to a repeatedly verbalized and steadfastly held stand that nothing was wrong.

Meanwhile, reports from instructors depicted increasing inability to make meaningful contact with people, instructors, staff, and worst of all, with patients, and a corresponding inability to synthesize what he knew in the clinical situation. For example, he made a diagnosis of diabetes mellitus without requiring a fasting blood sugar test. When questioned by a distressed preceptor, he responded readily that he knew this laboratory procedure was essential but was unable to explain why he had not prescribed it. No cognitive or paracognitive bridge had been made between the textbook knowledge and the clinical task. Physician-teachers and allied health personnel were dismayed and alarmed because chart notes were dangerously fragmented and incomplete. They emphasized that this was quite different from the problems they were familiar with, abbreviated or over elaborate student reports or careless or tardy reporting. Student M's chart notes, like his cognitive processes, seemed disconnected and could not safely serve as a basis for patient care.

There were other more subtle, but consistently reported findings. The student had great difficulty making and maintaining eye contact even for very brief periods, and peculiar gestures of the hands, facial grimaces, and inappropriate laughter made everyone uncomfortable for and with him. If faculty were distressed, patients were quick to respond. More and more they complained about the student and refused to be seen by him.

The numerous conferences about this student eventually came round to the question, "How did he ever get into medical school?" All faculty and staff were convinced that M's unsuitability should and could have been picked up during admission procedures.

Summary.   This student displayed a sizeable deficit in ego function, a formidable psychiatric problem. Additionally, his behavior strongly suggested an immature ego-ideal or one crippled by an almost complete lack of motivating shame or sense of inner requirements about trying to do physicianly things. Following postulates stated earlier, we hypothesized that modes for management of nurturance and needs for omnipotence had at best been only partially completed; tolerance for uncertainty and the capacity for empathic communication as judged by patients' responses were grossly inadequate. There were insufficient elements of mastery from the first three lines for the needed synthesis of physician ego-ideal at the time of medical school, but this situation only became apparent when clinical contact began. Student M had mastered the cognitive preclinical skills with the same success and via the same routes he had used to learn premedical materials and to achieve high scores on MCAT and other tests in admissions procedures.

This sketch is a stark picture in which there are deficient paracognitive supports for clinical work at all levels. It represents a point at one extreme of the educational spectrum, i.e., an instance where cognitive and paracognitive developments are grossly out of phase, and the paracognitive lag precludes further medical education. In spite of this developmental retardation, there was preservation and a sufficient coalition of cognitive and paracognitive abilities to achieve admission to medical school. But the subsystems represented by lines 1, 2, and 3 existing in incomplete, fragmented condition, could not be elaborated, controlled, or helped to become guiding and autonomous forces in the formation of a physician ego-ideal.

2. Unresolved Conflict in the Development of the Ego-Ideal

For Student O as for Student M, inability to master clinical work resulted in the possibility that medical training might have to be interrupted or even concluded. Like M, Student O rebuffed many varied offers of help from faculty, staff, and even peers; but his style was different. Proffered assistance was deflected or fended off rather than becoming the target for outright rejection, anger, or denial.

And there were other major dissimilarities. Unlike M, Student O was manifestly depressed rather than isolated and subtly withdrawn, and the depression was sufficiently profound and exposed to elicit fears about suicide from nonpsychiatrist faculty members. Sometimes this student was punctual and faithful in presenting himself for educational work, even though he was inaccessible psychologically. Intermittently, but not infrequently, he would "go underground," presumably stressed beyond a threshold which no one could perceive. He would fail to appear for academic or clinical commitments for periods as long as ten days and during these times was unresponsive to telephone and written requests for information about his condition and intents. At times he would actually leave the city.

These moratoria seemed to provide some personal relief, but exacerbated the worsening academic situation. Student O's performance was not only below acceptable levels in clinical areas, he had also failed to complete a number of curricular units and some major hurdle examinations, those where levels necessary for advancement were specified by school policy.

There was another point which differentiated Student O clearly as representative of a different point on the continuum of ego-ideal development from that of our first example. M was untouched (at least manifestly) by faculty criticism. He consistently and calmly ascribed the difficulties to bad teaching, failure to allow him adequate autonomy, or personal limitations in the instructors which made them unable to give him the support he needed to gain confidence. O, however, was unable to tolerate even the most thoughtful and constructive criticism. Instructors reported that at the first hint of judgment he became agitated and oppositional, unable to hear the issues as anything but a personal rebuke. He was thus unavailable for learning.

Summary. The nature of Student O's dilemma was clear enough to evoke an insightful remark from a classmate: "I think he can't decide whether or not he wants to be a doctor and would like someone else to settle it for him." Inner uncertainty about whether he *could* become a doctor—know enough, be competent enough, be authoritative enough—were some of the sources of his depression, with extensive roots (we would expect) in much earlier experiences. His conflicted ambivalence had resulted in so little progress along the omnipotence-uncertainty dimension that he once questioned the clinical judgment of an experienced instructor, who was stunned and puzzled at the student's obvious lack of a sense of appropriateness and reality.

The coincidence of beginning academic decline and clinical work was similar to that for Student M. O, too, had had few difficulties in preclinical studies. But the evident if partial interface of his psychological problems with learning seemed a hopeful sign. In this student, the relationship between cognitive and paracognitive universes was intact; the membrane was still permeable. The developmental failure in the ego-ideal was in large part a distortion, specifically a reversal, of the monitoring-shaming function. The noncommitment to a program of medical studies and the projection of that program's requirements as belonging to others (ego-alien) rather than as standards for internalization displayed some of the ways in which Student O's physician ego-ideal functions were failing to mature. Perhaps a dynamic exploration would have revealed major disjointures and delays in mastery of the first three lines; The unresolved conflict about medicine as his calling might have been a critical determinant which prevented the beginning coalescence of existing developmental elements into a physician ego-ideal. The resulting deceleration and threatened failure of professional growth had retarded and prevented the adequate acquisition and synthesis of knowledge.

3. Successful Resolution of Conflict Around the Ego-Ideal

Student P had been training in a paramedical field and was consciously surprised to discover he had been admitted to medical school after an impromptu application. There was no time for psychological preparation; he was plunged into medical school without the extensive anticipation, fantasies, and anxieties most students experience. Still, this fact alone did not seem to account for the scholastic emergency in which he found himself after some months. Its observable aspects were essentially similar (insofar as they could be measured) to those of Students M and O: incomplete work, failure to pass essential examinations, and erratic clinical skills usually not at the level necessary for his stage of training.

Student P did not withdraw, nor did he blame his instructors. Though depressed, he was mainly baffled, unable to understand the first academic failure of his life in spite of what he and the faculty acknowledged was ample intellect. In a short time, and with encouragement, he sought out several faculty members with whom to explore the puzzle. The answers came as he talked with one physician-instructor who advanced the idea that P seemed unclear about whether he wanted to be a doctor or continue training for his previous profession. Recognizing at once that this was the dilemma, and a choice he needed to consider, P began to work at disentangling his motives and goals. After a time he decided for medicine and presented to the faculty an outline of his plans to

remedy his academic deficiencies so that he could do what he enjoyed most, "taking care of patients." The presentation conveyed an
unclouded sense of purpose the faculty had not seen before.

Summary.   Student P represented a point on the continuum of
ego-ideal development further along in the direction of phase-
appropriate progress than the two previous examples. Though conflicted, there were in this student counterforces sufficient to allow
him to cope with a crisis and reverse a declining scholastic course.
The distinctions among these three examples are worth reviewing.

Unlike Students M and O, P was accessible to faculty assistance,
recognized the problem clearly as his, and felt that the responsibility for its resolution was also his. These two facts alone bespeak an
inner cohesion, monitoring and organizing trends which mark a
level of maturity not reached by many medical students. General
developmental progress had occurred along with advances toward
mastery of the first three lines of development. After all, medical
students and physicians are not unique in the tendency to ascribe
failure to the environment or to find it comforting to believe that
the sources of conflict and frustration lodge in others more than in
themselves. The capacity to look inward is always more difficult
when assaults upon self-esteem come from the outside, and this
capacity is one for which many need supportive help.

Student P displayed definite, if just perceptible, evidence for a
beginning physician ego-ideal. His decision to continue in medical
school, his comprehensive, well-organized plan to "catch up" which
so impressed the faculty (and rightly), and his certainty about where
the most satisfaction lay for him were points in his favor. It was his
beginning awareness, if only dimly or preconsciously perceived,
about the cluster of standards that a doctor should hold for himself
which enabled P to synthesize his commitment to the calling. Using
previously unrecognized strengths from the first three lines and
helped by suitable supportive faculty members, who were also
proper targets for identification, he became aware that something
within him, which we have called the ego-ideal, already bore the
stamp of physician.

4. A Dyssynchronous Ego-Ideal

Student Q received mixed educational reviews. Whenever faculty discussed their choices for the best student in the class, his name was sure to be mentioned. Though he was infrequently the choice as top student, he was always ranked in the top 5 percent. His test performances were outstanding, but judgments from a variety of clinical settings reported some unevenness in excellence. He rated above average in the usual cognitive domains such as the acquisition and retention of facts and was considered (independently of test results) bright, energetic, and conscientious. But like all of the students we have portrayed in this section he did not come to trouble because he lacked intellective ability. A number of instructors were puzzled by a kind of dispersion in student Q's knowledge; in clinical encounters he seemed unable to distinguish relevant from irrelevant findings. It may be argued that this capacity is almost always slow to develop and becomes more rapid, automatized, and skillful only with experience. But it was just this kind of improvement which had not happened in Q. As months and years of medical school progressed, he remained diffuse in his handling of clinical data.

Although only partially aware of his difficulties, this very bright student had evolved some coping maneuvers to deal with them. For example, since he could not readily discern order or levels of importance in clinical data, he compensated when called upon by presenting everything he knew. This protective strategy elicited varying responses from his teachers: admiration, impatience, annoyance, and, with time, concern. Often in the welter of knowledge, there would be a void. Whenever these lacunae in the data base were encountered, and they became more frequent as clinical training went on, the responses from all involved became more agitated, especially the student. He would set about correcting the newly uncovered deficiency with a speed which suggested desperation. At any cue that there was something he should have known and didn't, Q could with certainty be found in the library, laboratory, record room, or media center at his first free moment. He would return from these forays with a deluge of facts which seemed to reassure him. His instructors, however, were not particularly comforted; they were left with a mystery. If this student was so conscientious and bright, how had it happened that an encounter with a patient had not already triggered the curiosity which should have led him to search out, master, and have available the needed information?

Another stratagem used by this student was his need to ingratiate himself. This behavior pattern was an odd mix. Student Q was eager to learn, a quality which evoked praise and admiration from his peers and teachers. But often this eagerness seemed motivated more by the desire for academic progress than by emerging professional maturation. When a given point was raised, Q would often say that this was an area he'd been wanting to explore—but the enthusiasm was not implemented. Still later this content area might surface as one of his "empty spots." This characteristic, among others, caused some of his preceptors to question his ingenuousness, to wonder why he was still garnering knowledge to impress and not yet seeking knowledge for use in healing.

Summary. The temporary arrest in development described here is an example of a malformed physician ego-ideal. In Student Q the part of his personality we have called the physician ego-ideal had become concentrated on standards needed for being a good student. There was little evidence of a readjustment of priorities so as to enable a shift to the requisites for being a good doctor. This man was more attuned to external than to internal standards and to cognitive rather than clinical goals. We could not tell in students with these kinds of problems whether they felt the two sets of internal requirements were identical. But if so, this occurred in the face of consistent input from faculty that there were important, indeed vital, distinctions. Because he was so intent upon being a good student, Q had not been free to enjoy the liberty of pursuing his own ideas and curiosity, and this was at least one important factor in causing the information gaps discussed above. Independent, self-directed learning had, for this student, apparently been perceived as secondary to the implied or even explicit desires of teachers.

As in previous examples, the etiology of this developmental problem, the distortion in physician ego-ideal, lay in incomplete mastery of the earlier lines of development. Q had hardly begun to resolve the problems of the omnipotence-uncertainty dimension, much less make his peace with them; he had settled for pseudocertainty and amnesia (or repression) for gaps in his store of information. This explained for us his inability to order data or distinguish relevant from nonproductive information as readily as his peers. Lacking this first-order ability, he was naturally hampered in formulating a picture of the case, an ordered problem list or an integrated diagnosis, and without these conceptual staples, proper management and patient care was a struggle.

As he progressed further in medical studies his conviction (perhaps faith is not too strong a word) that knowing as much as possible made a good medical student and doctor was confirmed in another way. He began to speak with a certain oracular quality; classmates complained that he was patronizing. Some instructors felt that he really abhorred any situation in which he did not know all the answers and that an exaggerated fear of such situations made him nervous and caused his performance to suffer. One fact was plain: Student Q had been unable to accept at a feeling level the idea that there are occasions on which a doctor cannot be omniscient and that the most mature approach to medical practice and medical knowledge includes a reasonable tolerance for uncertainty.

There were other delays in early lines of development, many of them predictable from the material above. Engrossed in the struggle to know as much as possible, he seemed to have suffered some atrophy in the capacity to implement nurturant impulses. Most faculty reports about students, even those in average ranges, included the comment that the individual showed concern for patients, that he really "cared" about them. Not one such comment could be found about Q. The objectivity-empathy dimension seemed similarly skewed. Valuing objectivity as an indispensable component of omniscience, this student, although never unkind or brusque with patients, found it difficult to empathize with them.

We wish to be very clear about the kinds of difficulties we are describing. Most faculty felt that the capacity to develop adequate nurturance and the oscillation between objectivity and empathy were within the grasp of this student. But these capacities had in a sense been shouldered aside by a preoccupation with knowing and thus were only partially and insufficiently elicited. As we have said in previous sections, the vicissitudes of maturation in the earlier three lines bear a crucial relationship to the inner goals which form the physician ego-ideal. Furthermore, as in other developmental snags, the process is circular. Incomplete mastery of the first three lines inevitably interferes with the evolving physician ego-ideal, line 4. As the poorly developed ego-ideal becomes operative, it tends to reinforce existing patterns and militate against a reexamination of the earlier stages which might lead to better balance.

5. *Advanced Development of the Physician Ego-Ideal*

Appropriate or accelerated development is, as we have stated earlier, more difficult to document than are anomalies of growth. The differences between Students Q and R, for example, were impressive but not readily apparent. Contrast will provide the most cogent evidence for differentiating the two.

Patterning in "objective" measures such as examinations, scores, and formal ratings were virtually indistinguishable. In instructors' ratings, indeed, Q's record was slightly superior. It was when preceptors detailed the bases upon which they made their judgments that differences began to surface. Very early in his clinical work teachers remarked that Student R, though lacking knowledge and experience, was able to put together enough to give good medical care. Independent judges felt that in this capacity he was well ahead of his peers. Like Q, R was reported as bright and conscientious, but with an emphasis on organization of information, reliability, and steady, hard work. Unlike Q, R kept himself well read through independent study in addition to being in good command of material from assigned reading.

Work with patients followed a similar pattern. Student R's concern for them was mentioned often, and the thorough and persistent way this work was undertaken was considered exceptional. Even his chart notes, which represent a task of which few physicians are enamoured, were completed promptly, kept up to date and in order. His punctuality was notable. Routine physicals and follow-up checks were consistently pursued to closure, i.e., until he was satisfied that all that should have been done had been done. Increasingly, judgments about what was necessary to reach this closure point came from the student and sometimes exceeded faculty expectations.

From early in his training, R's capacity for handling volumes of clinical work attracted attention, a finding consistent with his penchant for organization and devotion to care. One preceptor noted that this student saw considerably more patients in a given time period than his colleagues; another wrote that as training progressed R began to speak of how busy he was with the same combination of pride and weariness that is often heard from practicing physicians. When consulting with preceptors about his patients, he behaved and was treated more and more as a colleague than a student. Several instructors stated that R was well professionalized before graduation, additional evidence of advanced maturity.

Though courteous and well-liked by teachers, R did not seem to feel the need to ingratiate himself. If he differed with preceptors about some issues of patient management, his response would be candid; he would put forward his reasoning and the evidence for it with conviction. And when occasionally he was left unconvinced by the preceptor's response the feeling came through, but clearly it was a matter of professional disagreement, not personal pride.

He knew the range of his knowledge well. Assertive when sure of this data, he was never oracular. He seemed to have accepted and internalized before graduation the concept that one may, in fact, must, be in command of quantities of medical information, but never without an awareness of the limitations of such information. So geared, Student R could seldom be stampeded into a rash statement or a thoughtless judgment and never seemed to panic when his ignorance in a given area was uncovered. His stand in these circumstances was a combination of poise and resolute diffidence which enabled him to say quite clearly that he did not know what was being asked, was eager to hear what the teacher knew, and intended to read in the area himself as soon as feasible.

Summary.   As our sketch of this student illustrates, advanced maturation and the progress toward a physician ego-ideal has many of the same features found in advanced development generally. There is mastery and consolidation of earlier stages, in this sequence, lines 1, 2, 3. For example, R's tendency to organize data represented a psychological command of the need for omnipotence. Faced with a problem, he could pause, and during the delay, thoughtfully scan the extent of his information. His behavior reflected emotional (in contrast to verbal or intellectual) acceptance of the fact that there are limits to the knowledge any doctor can master. For the rest, he must operate as comfortably as he can on the basis of probabilities, concentrating on gaining skills and judgment which will enable him to estimate the importance of these probabilities. This student's methodical, almost relentless, devotion to patient care represented a highly appropriate and effective transmutation of the need to be nurturant. With such unusual progress in resolution of problems of earlier phases, acceleration to more complex integrations was unimpeded and had already carried R well beyond his peers at graduation.

Again, there are two points which cannot be made too often. The student himself seemed little aware of the state of affairs we have described. He was busy at the task of learning doctoring and less interested in how he compared with others than in establishing standards for himself. Yet the strength of his tie to the calling of medicine had been observable as early as the sophomore year. Even then he was able to pull together from a small and circumscribed store of skills and knowledge enough of the stuff of physicianhood to deliver good patient care. These kinds of data are manifestations of a changing internal mental apparatus—the physician ego-ideal.

The sequenced roster of examples which have ended this chapter were chosen to illustrate the breadth of developmental range that can be observed. They were also selected to make another point, especially evident in the last example: The successfully maturing physician ego-ideal is clearly the herald of physician identity.

Developmental Line 5: Maturation of an Operational Professional Identity

Since its appearance in *Childhood and Society* in 1950, Erikson's term *identity* has suffered all the outrages of instant popularity. It was seized upon with frenzy by health professionals and the general public, commented upon endlessly from lecterns and pulpits and quoted even by the Pope, used in situations for which it was never designed and in attempts to accomplish conceptual tasks for which it is inappropriate. If a battered-term syndrome exists, *identity* is indeed a candidate for the designation. Perhaps it was Erikson's acute, poetic approach to the idea which resulted in the danger that the term might become depleted of precise meaning. But, as with most accurate and sound notions, *identity* survives, and Erikson has aided in its resuscitation by assaying definitions, redefinitions, and clarification (1975). Redefinition, our first task, will combine Erikson's efforts with material thus far assembled.

The best place to start is where Erikson does, in the earliest phases of human development. The first "developmental position" (1975, pp. 210–11), which we have discussed at several points, is one in which the main issue is basic trust versus basic mistrust. In his revisitation, Erikson emphasizes a point with special importance for physician identity. This initial stage is one in which the infant as a condition of life develops an "unbroken sensory eagerness." We are convinced that the tie between this "unbroken sensory eagerness" and its eventual implementation in the physician's broad perceptual scan is necessary for good medical work. Another feature essential for maturation in the early months of life is the presence of "a *reliable* parent image" (Erikson 1975, italics ours). It is only if parenting figures are constant that there is "the development of hope," a concept similar to or synonymous with object constancy as described by Mahler (1968) and A. Freud (1958). This can also be thought of behaviorally: basic trust builds over time as the infant reaffirms and ascertains that parenting figures will be available as they are needed and will provide gratification and regulation in ways that are gentle and internalizable, thus facilitating homeostasis. As this happens, the capacity to accept both gratification and limits increases.

In chapter 6 we described at length the evolution of the ego-ideal. As this portion of the self-concept becomes embedded in a psychosocial matrix, identity formation begins. The development of an ego-ideal is essentially an intrapsychic matter; identity formation is a psychosocial phenomenon. For doctors as well as for others it is a vocational validation, a verification of useful aspects of the ego. Any comfortable accommodation of person and work will qualify for this definition of a successful work identity. It remains to specify how this good fit is different for physicians. Before going further, some obvious but necessary ground rules are needed.

It is barely sufficient to say that there are many underlying physician identities. In this account we will use the singular *identity* as a generic term. It is not validly descriptive or accurate, much less inclusive, but despite the apologia, must hold for the present. Variegation in physician identities is another story. There are deficiencies in all of the English words used to describe the kind of complex developmental amalgamations we are attempting to encompass. One could say that identity is a mosaic; we have repeatedly said it is an intertwined meld of many strands. It is another testimony to the robustness of the concept that etymologic obstructions cannot obscure it. The process can be itemized temporally as follows: The bits and makings of identity begin to accumulate as does the grout of psychosocial placement. They cluster, combine as elements, and finally fuse into a stable unit. As numbers of these nuclei accrue to the personality, the identity structure gains strength, assumes its unique character, and is maintained and enhanced in much the same constellation throughout professional life. Only occasionally is it altered, and rarely in medicine.

An everyday event can be used to intersect this temporal process. If a ten-year-old comes upon a wounded bird, the gamut of responses can easily be predicted. Some children, frightened or disgusted, will flee; others whose fear and disgust are mixed with currents of sado-masochistic affects may stamp on the bird. Depending upon how far along morality has developed, how guilt has been deployed for accountability, and how large a role introspection, self-observation, and words have played in upbringing, the destructive act may be accompanied by the thought that it is a good idea "to put it out of its misery." Other children will pick up the bird briefly, then relinquish it; some will try to mend a broken foot or wing and even seek help in the rescue from parents, veterinarians, a local naturalist. Those who display the latter behaviors, the examiners and fixers, are examples of early and as yet incomplete clusters of physician-identity elements. And this is especially true for those youngsters impelled to marshal assistance from adults. Such behaviors constitute indicative precursors of substance and urgency, because at this age these are the only ways in which a beginning physician-identity can operate and because they show that the nascent identity already has momentum enough to begin to try. Unlike the physician who may result some ten or fiteen years later, there are no appropriate skills, no issues of responsibility, quality of care, or deep implementable concern over outcome. That would be too much to expect.

As we (R. Zabarenko et al. 1970) and others have noted, medicine seems to be a profession in which many people become passionately involved; once firmly engaged, fewer physicians leave than do professionals in other callings. Attorneys often enter tangential paths, become involved with enforcing justice or generating and interpreting laws which do so, or framing large-scale policies to implement justice as social good, e.g., politics. They may diverge even further and become businessmen or managers. Clergymen may have difficulty maintaining their identity if moral concerns collide or interfere with impulses toward nurturance or if they are beset by doubts. Like Dr. K in chapter 5, they may come to wonder if they are "good enough" or were truly called. Of course doctors also doubt the fiber of their identity—and some need to abandon it—but by comparison, the physician identity is strong. We propose that there are at least two sources for its power. One is the enormous social value placed on the profession; second are numerous developmental surges and confirmed psychic structures such as those we have been describing. It is a combination—less an arithmetic summation than a calculus of integrations of many forces—which gives physician identity its tenacious resilience.

Trace evidence of these vectors of forces can be observed before medical school. In chapter 2 we spoke of three early but significant decisions on the path toward physicianhood. The last was the public declaration of intention, defined as the act of applying for medical school. Once the declaration for physician identity is made, many can renounce it only with great difficulty. Something of the power and magnetism which the hope and longing for the physician identity has generated even at this point can be seen most plainly when its fulfillment is endangered. Those who do not gain admission to medical school often apply persistently for many years after the initial refusal. Another large group, barred from one customary route, go to medical schools outside the United States, knowing that this is expensive and time consuming and that reentry to the U.S. medical community is difficult and attenuated. Some medical school applicants are driven to outright dishonesty. A recent professional publication for medical educators contained the information that thefts of admission tests and criteria were increasing and urged vigilance on the part of those responsible for the security of these documents.

When the unavailability of medicine is clearly established, many of those excluded from it experience a bitter, "if-only" vocational aftertaste. Some seem never truly to attain a palate for the work in which they settle, even when it brings success as measured in most conventional terms. Often these individuals, disappointed for themselves, seek gratification in the hope that an offspring will want to become a physician.

Some authors (e.g., Becker 1961) have proposed that the physician identity, like many professional identities, becomes truly operational only when the student has passed through all the stages of apprenticeship and assumed professional responsibility. Yet again, observations from the field suggest that the matter is not so simple. It seems more likely that when internal developments reach a certain intensity and interact with and are reinforced by powerful social sanctions, the result is a critical mass which is the beginning of physician identity. This intersection is further accentuated by the long history of the calling and the heavy institutionalization of progress to and through it.

We have tried in chapter 6 to depict the extensive, obstacle-filled course which medical students have always (in the historical sense) had to traverse. This tortuous route is mediated by institutions, most of them educational, at each point along the way; simultaneously the traveler is upheld by social approval and the whole is supported (fiscally and otherwise) by society. Some might say that the reasons for societal support are obvious: The essence of a culture lies with its priests, healers, and lawgivers. Whatever the reasons, institutional formalization and cultural shoring further strengthen the formation of the physician's ego identity. Paradoxically, this state of affairs also contains some of the explanations about the poor quality of some of its products.

Even though defects in the capacity for becoming a good physician can be recognized early in medical training and with sufficient care before admission to medical school, high risk candidates, likely to become second-rate doctors, are often admitted. And once admitted, heroic and sometimes downright bizarre amounts of time and energy are expended in salvage efforts. Having entered the formidably institutionalized and strongly sanctioned conveyor toward physicianhood, students are retained who might falter without such strong identity- and life-support systems and who perhaps might better be permitted to do so. In other fields of graduate education, mortality is not only permitted, it is expected. In the basic life and behavioral sciences, for example, a student's failure causes neither the guilt nor shocked surprise which often plagues medical school faculty under similar circumstances. In fact, in many graduate schools, such losses are sometimes seen as creditable—chilling but unmistakable proof that the program demands much and that not everyone can make the grade.

Perhaps this account of the epigenetic saga of physician identity seems over elaborate. It may appear that what is being described is the sort of professionalization which occurs in most vocations. There are serveral ways to rebut this view. One will take us a bit afield, but the path of evidence will return to target.

In our Western technocratic society, from which we both benefit and suffer, malignant depersonalization at work is a menace of erosive potency. Many who are employed do not derive their core identity from their jobs; nor are they meaningfully identified with what they supply or produce. Assembly-line factory workers who cannot take pride in what they help to produce will even less often be able to feel a part of or even understand the enormous scope and power of the multinational corporations whose existence their work supports. Left without such identificatory moorings, these people are vulnerable to the feeling that, like inanimate physical commodities, such as fuel and machines, they will be used by the corporate entity until they become fiscally unprofitable and will then be discarded. For those at elite vocational levels, such as highly skilled machine-tool operators or airline captains, the work is fiscally rewarding, may have an aura of glamour, and also elicit some commitment to excellence, but it still does not contribute substantially to identity.

Western society esteems work identities variously. Money may buy some marks of respect, but without identity validation—a well-paying job may still leave a deficit. Some pursuits, e.g., those tied to political power, or the uncertain flicker of fads as in some of the performing arts, are only as stable as the last venture—election, performance, or feat. These kinds of work-identity brinkmanship call for all but the most avid and ambitious or the vocationally mobile. As a result, major identity weightings come to lodge in other life spheres—a person's major self-concept is as parent, spouse, sportsman, volunteer, etc.

We are convinced that work has an especially durable significance in the professions. One synonym for profession is calling; and cynicism notwithstanding, this is frequently felt literally. The assumption is made that an individual is attracted to a profession. Responding to a magnetism whose nature he may understand poorly or not at all, he comes to try on the identity.

One of the psychological contrasts between the professions, the arts, and the identity-empty vocations is that in the first, the job becomes the major identity. Etymology holds some of the clues for this: To enter the work means professing. With his decision to train for a given field the aspirant proclaims, "I declare I will be doctorly, lawyerly, scholarly, etc." For medicine, as we have described above, the vocational fitting, the haberdashery of life's work, may go on at very early ages. And the garment or calling must be settled upon speedily and staunchly if there is to be a chance of entering the formalized educational structures necessary to make it permanent.

But there remains still a need to tease out some threads in the tangle of distinctions between the professions and the arts. No doubt this will seem a digression to some, but not to any reader who has worked through the recurrent, boggy question: How much of medicine is art and how much is science? Perhaps it has remained a riddle so naggingly unresolved because the idea of professionalism, which may be a linking or intervening variable with some value has never been given adequate room.

Unlike the physician, the artist is related to and identified by his product; often he is not vividly related to the people who perceive it. In fact in some artistic circles, the accusation of pandering to popular taste is a bitter epithet. Those so tainted are likely to be suspected of being not "true" artists but hucksters guilty of cheapening artistic expression for profit.

Another more significant sociocultural distinction is that, throughout modern history and in many of the greatest civilizations, artists have been excused from certain social taboos. They are often expected to be odd, eccentric, or at least temperamental. In return they are obligated and privileged to expose their inner thoughts. The contrast with medicine could hardly be sharper. For although artists are exempt from some restraints, they are not so firmly sanctioned as healers. The equation necessary for achieving a work identity by balancing social supports and inner forces is quite different from that of the doctor. For full expression the artist needs to feel it necessary, even imperative, to publicize inner states most often kept comfortably private and to do this even when there is meager tangible, current, societal reward. In medicine there is a reversal or counterpoint. Along with support for the calling, there is an escalated expectation for confirmation of conventional social values. Not only must the physician be reliable, but he must represent abstinence from selfish gain, the delight of gossip, and many other "ignoble" drives, (McLaughlin 1961).[1] One can see the compliance with these expectations in the conservative (and valid) way in which most physicians judge innovations, especially in matters of patient care. And the implicit, often unconscious, desire for conforming (or confirming) behavior also surfaces in the need of patients to see their doctors in conservative attire, a desire generally respected. College professors may teach in shorts, sweatshirts, and thongs; but these very professors, although loath to admit it, would probably not like to consult a doctor similarly outfitted. An example of gradual acquiescence to the needs of patients can be observed by watching sophomore medical students change from campus attire to "doctor garments" as they become increasingly involved with patients. In their first "examinations" in the physical diagnosis course a substantial number of the students appear in campus garb barely hidden under a short white coat. Some months later, as they come to feel that patients are "theirs," dress becomes increasingly sedate and formal.

---

1. One version of the Oath of Hippocrates includes the following: "Into whatever houses I enter, I will go into them for the benefit of the sick and will abstain from every voluntary act of mischief and corruption, and further from the seduction of females and males, of freeman and slaves . . . with purity and holiness I will pass my life and practice my Art."

The conservatism of costume has to do with constancy. As the patient in his illness regresses more deeply, it becomes increasingly important because more stability and reliability are required from the care-giver. Steadiness in the sense of appearing in a predictable visual form may come to be equated with dependability, and thus essential in an agent of comfort. The nurse's uniform serves an identical, valid, psychological need. This superficial phenomenon, dress, is only one indicator of the ways in which doctors and patients are bonded in a conscious and unconscious mutuality and validation of the psychosocial matrix. This is yet another linkage in the intra-psychic accretion which results in physician identity.

The stamina to carry on the day-to-day work is necessary and valued in medicine. In this sense doctors live out the historical strictures and traditions of their calling in daily work. It is an iden-tity element so firmly set as to represent a keystone. Physicians themselves seldom need to express it. The history of medicine, for example, is sometimes written by historically oriented physicians, but more frequently by historians. When physicians fall ill psychiat-rically, work may not come up in the course of the psychotherapy, because it often remains an area uninvolved in psychic conflict even after the illness has eroded other functions.

All these points emphasize the importance of the work identity to the total identity in physicians. Just as the British do not put the name of their country on their stamps, presumably because they were the first nation to think of the idea, doctors are almost never self-conscious about the history and traditions of their calling even though these are among the most venerable. Let there be no mis-take about this apparent casualness. Though they are not conscious of it as a given, physicians very deeply, and not always consciously, feel intensely about this.

If some of the requirements emanating from patients and from doctors for themselves seem irrational, their explanation loops back to the demand for reliability, especially in the face of illness, and to Erikson's point that there must be constancy before there can be confidence and hope. Earlier we pointed out that these are among the earliest human requirements and are thus extremely potent in all human relationships. All the more so for physicians—creative daring in a painter is admirable, but a doctor must be someone you can count on.

This raises another conundrum: How much of medical practice is creative? Let us define creativity crudely for the moment as the ability to make unexpected or unusual turnings in the path toward the solution of a task. As an issue for debate, this seems a straw man; as a dimension of physician-identity, it merits an illustration.

In the late 1940s a physician-patient in his mid-forties was admitted to a large state mental hospital with a psychotic picture consisting of extensive paranoid delusions, e.g., the walls were filled with microphones, people were spying upon him, and the attendants were disguised FBI agents sent to assasinate him. He was extremely agitated, feared attack and victimization, and responding to voices signaling danger, he paced wildly up and down in his room. Both the agitation and the delusions were difficult to control. Sedatives currently in use were prescribed in substantial and then large doses with virtually no effect. Further, over a period of approximately thirty days the patient's condition steadily deteriorated. His psychotic state had constantly deflected efforts at physical examination.

Because this state hospital also contained a research institute, it chanced that the patient was seen transiently and at a distance by an internist interested in research in the chemistry of psychopathology. The internist suggested, rather tentatively, a possible diagnosis of myxedema psychosis, a very rare entity and one especially unlikely in a physician. There was nothing, he said, to suggest this except a very slight thickening of the features of the patient's face, but as no other method or measures seemed to be achieving any success, the diagnosis was tested and found to be correct. A trial of thyroid medication was begun and within three to four weeks the patient was well enough to be discharged with an excellent prognosis so long as the condition was monitored and medication attended to.

The question is: In what way was the internist's diagnosis, which some would call "brilliant," akin to the artist's creative flair? Certainly his thinking about the patient and the disease had taken an unexpected turn, totally different from that of the psychiatrists who had examined the patient. Though they knew of the existence of this particular psychosis and, like the internist, were aware that its incidence was extremely low, none of them had managed to make the necessary diagnostic observations and integration.

This issue relates directly to physician identity. The achievement of a functioning physician ego-ideal, a backdrop for identity, offers the doctor a set of feasible standards to which he can hold himself. One of the cognitive results in most physicians is a hierarchy of probabilities which enable him to narrow the search for a diagnosis. Given a set of symptoms, he can reduce a large total number of possibilities, say two thousand, to four or five of maximal likelihood. It is the efficient scanning of the probabilities and the rapid detection of the most likely which makes medical work effective and economic. The capacity to which any given doctor can, however, always keep operational a secondary scan on the outliers, that is, the unlikely or uncommon diagnoses, is an element of identity and considered a hallmark of excellence.

But although *this* kind of creativity is present in the practice of medicine, the freely roving search for novel solutions is not. Nor is the full exploration of tantalizing serendipities. It is true that once a diagnosis is made and treatment decided upon, a certain relaxation does occur. The doctor is less stressed, usually responsible for carrying out a well-established routine and is thus more comfortable. This is akin to the "routine science" which follows "giant leaps" (Kuhn 1962). But there is little in medical work that is truly playful; the business at hand is much too serious. And this may account for the fact that doctors often become recreational enthusiasts outside the professional sphere and find these activities good mental hygiene. The only kind of play for physicians at work is the variety suggested by the following quote: "To contrive an answer to gnawing doubts was the highest joy. Indeed, there was a whole world of subdued gaiety and sober frolic in the playful subtleties of their . . . dialectic" (Howe 1976, p. 13, quoting from A. Heschel, *The Earth is the Lord's*). This quote was written to describe the world of biblical (Talmudic) study which existed in the poverty, fear, and isolation of the Eastern European ghettos. Its intriguing aptness for depicting medical sport suggests something of the severity of the hardships the two worlds share. There is nothing mystical or exegetic in doctoring; the ghetto was isolated from worldliness, illness is its grimmest essence.

It is time to return from clinical and everyday experience to conceptualizations. Identity is the capstone of adolescence. But there are three additional stages which seem to have been mislaid; they are barely mentioned and then only for the most part in highly technical psychiatric literature. To achieve the proper perspective, the sequence should be reviewed. Erikson saw identity as the issue of adolescence; intimacy versus isolation as the crisis of young adulthood; generativity versus stagnation as the dilemma of adulthood and the penultimate stage; integrity versus disgust and despair as that of maturity.

The beginning sentences of Erikson's description of the eighth stage, ego-integrity versus despair, make it clear how much, in his schema, identity is a way station: "Only he who in some way has taken care of things and people and has adapted himself to the triumphs and disappointments inherent to being, by necessity, the originator of others and the generator of things and ideas—only he may gradually grow the fruit of these seven stages. I know no better word for it than ego-integrity" (1959, p. 98). This extended quote represents additional ammunition for our efforts to delimit as well as define the concept of identity. The term has worn and frayed because it has been progressively diluted and less and less seen in the series in which it was first proposed. The achievement of identity seems to have expanded into a goal of life rather than a stage of growth.

One reason for this may be that few individuals attain the maturity of the eighth and ultimate stage, and thus it has been comforting, if slipshod, not to dwell upon it. One may go further and speculate that there is currently a certain malignant flimsiness of identity in general in Western civilization, and this unpromising state of affairs has drawn the attention of philosphers and developmental experts. That intimacy and generativity are only slightly less rare than ego-integrity is support for this hypothesis.

Progress toward physician identity is no more in reality the
smooth ascent shown in figure 7 below than are any of the other
lines of development. The curve shown in all of these figures is a
graphic generalization, a curve of best fit which averages out peaks
and troughs to show trend. But for the present discussion, a reversal
will be useful; a consideration of the timing and characteristics of
irregularities can add to our gradual and purposeful complication of
matters. In chapter 6 we began to discuss some of these processes as
they related to the physician ego-ideal.

The passing of important hurdles in medical training—national
certifying   examinations,   graduation   from   medical   school,
licensure—produces a developmental unevenness which can be described in three stages. There is anxiety and apprehension as the
hurdle approaches. After it is passed, there is a period of elation.
Admixed with this elation are elements of a new and yet familiar
kind of anxiety. The melody is the same, the words are different.
Before the hurdle the agony is: "Am I good enough to make it?"
After the hurdle has been passed and success and relief have ebbed, a
nagging doubt remains: "Am I really good enough to be what I am
now declared to be?" The declaration may be that the student is now
a junior, has received the M. D. degree, been licensed, or declared
a certified specialist. The questions and the affects are essentially
the same, as are the reactions to them in healthy development.
Subsiding elation and anxiety signal the consolidation of the new
state as a kind of preidentity nucleus. Each hurdle scaled converts
into an identity bit; part of consolidation includes fitting these bits
together into a meaningful whole.

It is suggestive and important that most medical students seldom
recall examination hurdles as important turning points in their
careers. Although the exams are felt with crushing urgency at the
time, and induce the sequences and feelings we have described,
they are viewed as obstacles, not growth. The students' affective
sense of validity has both confirmation and refutation in evidence.
Although remembered with distaste or erased by amnesia, the hurdle examinations may in fact be important for growth because they
enable the student to accrue the nuclei of physician identity in the

manner just described. On the other hand, grades in medical school, often determined by examination scores, are not the best predictors of performance as a physician, strongly suggesting that other events during medical training, perhaps remembered and perhaps not, are also, in other ways growth points. The skeptical will certainly enter here that this is nothing new; seldom is any individual aware of when or at what juncture he learned what he needed to master his profession. But that does not make the effort at discovery less worthwhile if the tracking leads to clues about how identity arrives at its destination.

There is another piece of evidence which bears on this point and which also can be observed during medical training. Students often do not correctly estimate the excellence of physicianhood in their teachers. Beause they are still in many ways at a developmental level appropriate to adolescence, i.e., struggling to establish an identity, they are apt to be captivated by the dashing, supremely confident teacher, one who may be in part showman. The steady, informed clinical teacher is often disdained as stodgy, plodding, and pedestrian.

When we ask why students make these kinds of judgments, the answer is to be found, as always, in the developmental state of things. The teacher who is flashy as well as competent, cocky as well as confident, commands the students' interest and becomes the target for identification because he does business with them at their own level. In part or temporarily he has the capacity to feel and think like an adolescent and to be in a properly regulated sense adolescent. The caliber of the sober, steadfast teacher is frequently unappreciated because he is unable to regress for the purpose of teaching to an earlier stage of identity formation.

At another level this has to do with a part of the oedipal triangulation we spoke of toward the end of chapter 4. The two prototypical clinician teachers just described represent different kinds of fathers. It is entirely predictable that students will be drawn to the adolescentoid rather than the adult father. He shows, with immediacy and dramatic effect, that he knows where they are, and where he is seems possible and desirable for them to reach.

Thus far much time has been spent in defining *identity* and *physician identity* and in conjectures with evidence about its development. There remain the problems of maintenance. DeLevita (1976) has advanced some concepts about the maintenance and derivation of identity which have special relevance to physician-identity. He proposes that identity derives from stimuli, "the reflections" which the individual (designated by DeLevita structurally as the ego) receives from others, and that these perceptive inputs are necessary for identity maintenance. These concepts fit well with what we have said earlier about the symbiotic relationship of the physician to his practice. The daily "reflection" from patients of his identity as "doctor" serves to confirm and support that identity. Just because this particular professional identity assumes great importance, the work itself becomes literally vital. The choice of adjective is carefully neutral. In most physicians the relationship to the practice is neither phoretic nor parasitic. Symbiosis is the most accurate conceptual version of the relationship available thus far.

Even as we consider the meanings and significance of maintaining the physician identity, definitions of commonly used terms are necessary, especially where precision has been blurred by usage patterns which suggest the words are interchangeable. Jung's *persona* (Singer 1972) and the omnipresent *role* are often substituted for or preempt *identity*. For us, the distinctions are important and can be briefly put. *Identity* is that sector of personality (ego) function which reflects and enables an acceptable psychosocial interfacing for beginning and carrying out adult tasks. *Persona* is closer to a statement about the type and quality of the psychosocial interface. *Role* is a word which carries strong contextual implications for the theater, is seldom carefully dissociated from these connotations, and usually means that which a person does for reasons of maintaining a maximal equilibrium in a social context. The incessant proliferation of related terms such as *role model, role identification,* and *role practicing* tend to obscure even further exactly what is meant.

Our goal in this chapter and the preceding one has been to be painstaking and persistent in our definitions of identity by culling and discarding the shabby, reordering useful, disarrayed elements, and adding theoretical constructs where there was a chance they might be incisive. At this point some reminders are in order. The total personal identity includes the physician identity amid other social roles. The fact that this work identity is especially important does not imply that it is the totality of a given doctor's identity nor that other callings do not have similarly important work identities.

The following vignette tells how the apportionment of physician identity and total identity existed in one doctor and how the ratio came to be discovered. A primary-care physician, accustomed to keeping his medical bag with him, attended a two-week sensitivity training session. His report about the experience was enthusiastic. There had been a garbage-throwing episode, some of his innermost and not very palatable thoughts and feelings were exposed, and he had joined in a drunken body-painting session with other seminar participants. He felt that the group techniques used had provided ample support for these unusual experiences and made them useful. One thing, however, bothered him. When he arrived, he had been forced, as part of the rules, to relinquish his medical bag; throughout the two weeks his work identity, like that of other participants in the seminar, was considered irrelevant unless he himself brought it up. Until he told them, other group members did not know that he was a physician, and they did not refer to him as "doctor." For this man, "throwing physician identity out of court" was traumatic, although eventually manageable. He came to know how much of him was "doctor," and how important his doctor bag was as a badge of his identity.

We have spoken above about some of the factors for maintenance of the physician identity, including DeLevita's (1976) perceptual reflections, but there are many more. Most doctors are unceasingly involved in identity grooming, preventive maintenance and enhancement, even though they may not think of it in this way. Continuing education was commonplace in medicine long before it became fashionable, let alone mandatory, for licensure or professional status. Again, medical custom and history are the root causes; it is a part of the original Hippocratic oath. Being out of date is a taboo for physicians. Maintaining the identity means remaining cognitively intact, in possession of recently uncovered knowledge, with physicianly skills well rehearsed. It is a matter of special pride to be able to continue or even increase one's capacity to make an unusual or rapid diagnosis, "to snag one from left field," as in the myxedema psychosis described above.

While identity is not the termination of either general maturational progress or professional development, the maintenance of identity is one achievement of adulthood, a foundation necessary for access to the last three stages of personal development. If our evidence about assiduous identity maintenance in medicine has been persuasive, it may seem reasonable that the possibility of going on to further developmental stages is improved for physicians and for others with large psychological investments in sustaining work identities.

The first four lines of development embody the features which make possible the establishment and maintenance of a physician identity sturdy enough to support a daily workload in which the stress of constant contact with disease, death, human pain, and suffering are at least as likely as cure and relief.

In the denouement of Barry's *Peter Pan*, there is a duel. Peter, cheered on by Wendy, the Boys and the Indian Princess, triumphs, of course. Holding Captain Hook at sword's point, he pauses, and the trembling, cowering villain asks, "Pan, who and what art thou?" The hero exults at the top of his lungs, "I'm youth, I'm joy, I'm freedom!" It is a perfectly consistent response from a character whose allegorical assignment is immaturity—he has vowed he will never grow up. The absence of the spirit of Peter Pan in physicians is a kind of negative of what we have been trying to say in this chapter. By its very nature, recalling how much we have stressed the importance of constancy, stamina, reliability, and stability, medical work contains little in it of what the playwright meant, the freedom to be juvenile.

This reverse literary analogy is our last piece of ideational evidence that achieving physicianhood means by its very essence that some of the components of adulthood have coalesced. In preceding chapters we attempted to describe the anatomy of identity. In this section our goal was to depict the final product—how the parts form the whole and how they are integrated for work. If the first four lines are analogous to anatomy, identity's metaphor is physiology: It encompasses both structure and function. It should therefore be no surprise that in selecting the clinical examples for this section we could not maintain the discipline and clarity of a time-slice sample, at least to the same extent as was possible for the previous four lines. The descriptions of the two physicians shown in figure 7 are less vignettes than abbreviated biographies, sketches meant to capture something of the life history of physician identity. Unhappily such evidence usually becomes available only when the life histories have become a part of case histories. But as an optimistic epilogue we can report that although both these doctors suffered some illness, both also made excellent recoveries. The opportunity to learn something about the roots of physician identity and what it meant to total functioning was a kind of accident or experiment in nature and healing. Furthermore, it is utterly consistent with historical traditions in science that important discoveries for normal functioning can be made via careful observations from pathology. Here then, with the usual deletions as a protection for anonymity, are two

FIGURE 7

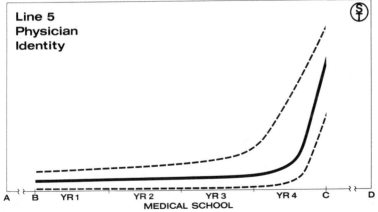

examples of the way in which physicianhood took root, built a support system, flowered and, after some setbacks and with assistance, thrived.

Drs. S and T had a great deal in common. Both were successful physicians as measured by any standard. But the one by which they, as do many other physicians, set the most store was an inner conviction about the excellence of their work. This was affirmed by the repute which they enjoyed among colleagues and in bulging practices and medical operations where grateful and often healed patients bore testimony to their commitment and devotion. There were similarities in early family constellations as well. Both men had fathers who were difficult to live with, needed to control their sons, and whose vocational pursuits were of a status usually considered inferior to medicine. Both had sickly mothers. In each case the "sickliness" was a nettling admixture of hypochondriasis, hysterical exaggeration, and confirmed disease processes which baffled most of the physicians asked to care for the patient and certainly the family involved with supporting her. Both men from earliest boyhood had wanted to be able to take care of their helpless, debilitated mothers and had admired their fathers; they felt the rivalry with them with a ferocity that could only be settled by a decisive victory. It is important that for these men victory did not mean alienation. It took the form of entering a profession about whose status there could be no question of altitude—it was higher than the father's. But neither rivalry nor triumph meant the obliteration of love, compassion, or empathy with their fathers.

The summary points are that these men had powerful cause to be attracted to and passionately identified with the idea of physicianhood. It is highly probable that physician-identity nuclei came into position and were firmly set by events within the family at very early ages, and the movement toward physicianhood was natural and adaptive if not inevitable.

With this history, it can hardly be surprising that as adults both men experienced difficulty in relationships with their wives and children and that the problems brought them to treatment. Lest we be accused of unworldliness we want to be clear that both Drs.

S and T were engaged in lucrative specialties. This facet of the whole is important; it probably contributed heavily to their discontent with their fathers' positions and aims and to their determination to outdo them. We will focus, however, upon the psychological matters principally; the sociology and economics of their implementation seem less relevant.

Dr. S's father was an independent, hardworking, successful business man—in the colloquial sense, self-made. Because of the nature of his work, he saw his young son rarely, and they had very few extended or regular times to spend with one another. But the boy always admired his father's quickness of mind and the way he could outdistance competitors by shrewdly and swiftly recognizing and capitalizing upon opportunities. The son observed these adventures mostly from his mother's bedside. The family arrangement was such that she came to rely upon her son for care.

This man's specialty as a physician was heavily intellectualized, one of those in which research work and publications are more apt to be the badge of distinction than empathic relationships with patients. In his dealings with patients he was compassionate, and his relationships with physicians, peers, and health-care teammates was an effective blend of warmth, tolerance, and most of all, adherence to the highest standards.

Thus far we have attempted to sketch a tree, now let us see if we can trace the roots—the lines of development. The oscillation between empathy and objectivity in this physician had successfully stabilized but not rigidified at a point toward the objectivity end of the continuum. The important point here is that alternation between objectivity and empathy was not only possible but a matter of daily exercise and routine. In a specialty often stereotyped as a haven for the cold and unfeeling, this physician could understand and cope with a patient's pain and anxiety and almost simultaneously perceive, decipher, and transfer highly technical information to the patient and to the colleagues needed to implement care. Considering the early opportunities, indeed the necessity, for implementation of nurturance (of his mother) it is not surprising that the specialty chosen involved little in the way of active, first-hand caretaking, but substituted instead a kind of refinement: an intellective, absolutely essential component provided to physicians who would be involved in the nurturant process directly. In the management of omnipotence the physician identity also reached unusual excellence. Part of what engendered the esteem and respect for this physician was the exquisite precision with which he both knew what he knew and also knew what neither he nor anyone else could know. And this was all the more impressive considering the volume of data which had to be sifted to arrive at such conclusions.

Bringing together the first three lines and bearing in mind the sketch above, it is not hard to guess how internal standards of excellence arose for this physician. It seems more important at this juncture to point out how well these served in the practice of his profession and how comfortable and resilient they were in the internal functioning of the physician identity and in his personal identity. He exhibited many of the characteristics we have discussed: Maintaining, with the help of colleagues and assistants, a vigilant surveillance of current literature, he was always eager to encounter and evaluate the latest technical developments, machines, procedures, devices in his field. But not until evidence had accumulated in what he considered sufficient amounts or until the innovation had been tried in his own institution and preferably in his own hands, was he willing to endorse or even permit its use with patients and then only if he could make what he considered an informed and intelligent judgment about the probable hazards and benefits involved.

Dr. T's father was a craftsman in a small town, a position whose aims and status came to be unthinkable as appropriate for the son. His medical identity came to reside in a tertiary surgical specialty which, at the time, had attracted a great deal of attention in the medical and public press. This was in part because it was a major surgical advance which, when successful, brought dramatic positive results in a condition whose prognosis had previously been poor. The work required a great deal of skill and swift assimilation of new techniques for proper execution.

Uncompromising about his requirements for excellence in the

operating theater, Dr. T was also relentless in his unwavering and devoted insistence on completeness in pre- and postoperative care. Like Dr. S, and many other tertiary medical specialists, he worked with a close-knit and well-organized team of physicians, nurses, and technicians. Part of the training of this team included detailed instruction in careful observation of patients preoperatively, meticulous psychological preparation for the surgery in such a way as to reduce anxiety as much as possible, and discussions with family and patients about what they might expect in the first postoperative days and during convalescence. His prestige as leader of a large team never prevented him from spending as much time as he felt necessary with an anxious preoperative patient or an apprehensive postoperative one. Commented one cynical patient, "How unlike a surgeon he is! He never seems to be in a hurry to get away." Although considered very possessive of his patients, the primary-care physicians with whom he worked were grateful for and sometimes astonished at how quickly and perceptively he could identify the point at which the time had come to begin turning patient responsibility back to them. And his obvious concern that this transfer should be complete but never abrupt was evident in a kind of yoking of care, usually made in the patient's presence, well in advance of the hospital discharge. As this evidence suggests, for Dr. T the capacity to be both objective and empathic were at very high levels. Undoubtedly the spatial separation of the operating room and the bedside made this possible in part, especially since the two arenas also meant an unconscious versus a conscious patient. But the fact of the response cannot be denied.

Regarding nurturance, the accounts of pre- and postoperative work offer ample evidence that both the implementation of nurturance and very high but feasible standards of performance were available to this physician. The management of omnipotence and uncertainty has an added edge of accomplishment if we recall that Dr. T was engaged in a specialty and procedure impressive to physicians and dazzling to many patients. In his work with families, attending physicians, and to an appropriate degree with patients, he was firm and consistent in emphasizing the limits of the techniques he was using, the potential risks involved, and his inability to guarantee cure.

Again, as in Dr. S's case, individual balances had been struck along points of a continuum in the mastery of the first three lines. An idiosyncratic pattern of feasible standards in the form of a physician ego-ideal had been forged. It was a tool comfortable enough for everyday work and also amply robust to serve as the foundation upon which to erect a physician identity of stamina and versatility.

CHAPTER 8

The Tree at Last

The very exercise of creating a framework to order and better understand development of any kind is useful, if only for the authors who propose it. To make a serious claim on anyone else's attention, however, a plan of this sort must offer more than evidence of a wish for self-improvement. As we have tried to make clear, these ideas were the result of discovery, data processing, conceptual work, trial-and-error engineering, graphic architecture, and luck. Their ultimate value remains to be determined, but they were stimulated by observations of real educational deficits and prodded by the conviction that these could be remedied best by more adequate understanding. The effort was never a theoretician's odyssey; the problems seemed too serious, too long neglected, and too pressing to permit such luxury.

In this final chapter we provide some hints and suggestions for possible uses—preliminaries more akin to line drawings than to finished models or proper structural representations. Work leading to more finished results is in progress and will be alluded to as illustrations of directions in which research might go. There are, however, uses for the developmental lines which need not wait. Though straightforward and unadorned by statistical restraints and parameters, they can provide the beginnings of quantitative refinements of the ideas adequate enough to demonstrate some practical possibilities.

We will begin with a review of concepts, including some which encompass promises made in early chapters and some which acknowledge promises yet to be kept. Next we will discuss three ways in which the developmental lines can be used: (1) as a way of tracking a medical student's paracognitive development in much the same way height and weight charts are used in pediatrics; (2) as a way of mapping students' progress in a more complicated two-dimensional framework which takes into account a comparison of his performance with that of his peers in terms of probability and also accommodates numbers of judges and the variability of judgments. This second discussion acknowledges the necessity, indeed the urgency, for quantifying measurement at the earliest opportunity and for attempting to encompass the variety in both the skills and depth at which paracognitive development can be assessed. The observers usually charged with this task are faculty. For most of them, teaching has been grafted onto a primary life work as healer, and evaluation, with its (unfortunately necessary) emphasis on detail and paper work, is viewed with minimal enthusiasm. As though this were not sufficient, the kind of evaluative work suggested here does not involve simple kinds of judgment, an almost absurd understatement. Given the facts, the accuracy and precision with which faculty have made these complex judgments using scraps of time snatched from more valued activities is remarkable, as will be demonstrated below. This may be in part because similar life experiences and developmental paths provide them with ready inner sets of criteria against which to compare and report.

If the developmental ideas we have proposed are useful, it must also be recalled that, unlike height and weight, we cannot as yet provide a ratio scale for the lines, nor agreement on criteria, although we hope that the preceding chapters have suggested where the work may begin. And we need to devise the means to begin to reflect if not depict the largesse of freedom in standards as well as criteria used by the faculty to arrive at these judgments. Hence our third topic: (3) we view this situation as a challenge to produce measurement devices sufficient to the task. They should approximate the depth and richness of the thinking involved, in a multidimensional framework meant to underscore the fact that the schema we have set out is not best thought of as a set of separate growth curves or even a cluster or nest of overlapping phases. Ultimately it is more accurately conceived of as a series of currents, pushed at differing speeds through varying terrains and channels, dividing but mostly combining in ways which can at best be estimated only indirectly. If this last statement resonates a sense of complexity compounded with less exactness than might be desirable, that is as it should be, and the fact should be no more surprising than any proper description of an elaborate natural process.

An hydraulic topographical analogy can serve as well as any other. It is possible to trace the main course of the Colorado River by drawing a line on the map. If that representation seems sparse, information showing feeder streams and elevations of surrounding areas will make the picture less bare. But to capture even a fraction of the natural phenomenon under discussion would require additional data about ecological balances, continental air flow patterns, geological eras, and much more. Furthermore, to convey to an unfamiliar observer the excitement, profundity, and even a portion of the meaning of the river and its geography would require careful study and a substantial understanding of the results of the forces listed above. It would have to include, for example, explanations, historical currents, and predictions about the stunning spectacle of the Grand Canyon, the urgent aridity of eastern Colorado, the salinity problem at the Mexican border. It is this kind of ambitious descriptive scope that we shall aim for in the third illustration.

Concepts Revisisted

A review of concepts, as promised, must precede a description of these three kinds of utilization. In the last section of chapter 2 we said, "The first three lines represent the kind of developmental progress seen in the early stages of many types of complex learning. The last two, slower to begin, slower to mature, more rarely approaching the highest levels, seem of a supraordinate variety. Like the others, they build upon previous stages and involve the necessity for synthesizing previous learning and experience." Figures 8 and 9 display these two families of curves.

FIGURE 8

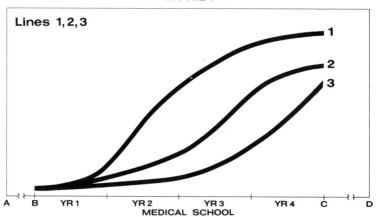

An important fact not shown in these graphs relates to the variance around the lines which can be seen in figures 3–7 above and in figures 10–12 shown later in this chapter. The latter group of figures reiterates, among other things, two points: (1) The first three lines have relatively similar and apparently symmetrical amounts of

FIGURE 9

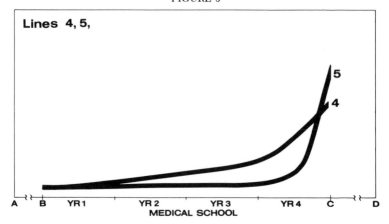

variance in terms of educational feasibility. (2) There is much greater variability in the mastery of lines 4 and 5, and the variability, at least as we estimate it during the undergraduate years of medical training, is asymmetrical with a positive trend, i.e., many more students seem capable of developing in the ranges above the central tendency. These notions are consistent with the propositions that lines 4 and 5, the development of a physician ego-ideal and the growth of physician identity, are more complicated than the first three, and with the descriptive and theoretical material suggesting that overall variance is greatest for physician identity. Points made in chapters 6 and 7 about the powerful forces activated within students relative to medicine as a calling may be at least in part an explanation for the fact that the asymmetrical distribution of variance for lines 4 and 5 is in the direction of advancing development. Perhaps development in these lines is advanced by the social forces in medical training which foster their growth. These shaping activities are available to conscious mental processes.

We cannot responsibly proceed without reminding the reader of the large amounts of developmental charting and discovery which are spanned in all graphs between points A and B, and C and D. The abrupt interruption of these lines was meant to symbolize at least two additional projects earmarked for future attention but only touched upon telegraphically in this work. We have repeatedly alluded to but have not in any way attempted to describe adequately the organismic substrata of events common to all human development which lead eventually to the currents of development toward physicianhood, the A to B section of the graphs. The literature in this area is excellent and evocative (e.g., Knight 1973, Fredericks and Mundy 1976) and has been referred to briefly. But still it seems to hold only the clues to directions for future investigations in the specific area of this study.

One way to test and correct our hypotheses about the sequences leading to physicianhood during medical school would be retrospective studies in which medical students and physicians could be encouraged to focus on retrieving memories of early life experiences and the ways in which these contributed to their choice of career.

The need for this kind of study has special urgency because it might add data of value to the predictive work involved in selecting students for premedical studies and admission to medical school. More carefully detailed studies of children's feelings and behaviors toward doctors are needed, in addition to carefully designed reconstructive studies using groups of participants with no evident psychopathology who are already engaged in medical education. Longitudinal studies of how early nurturance was received and then reenacted, the universally played "doctor game" (Simmel 1926), the allure of the calling and finally affixation to it throughout the transformations of latency and adolescence—all of these are areas where thorough investigation is scanty, if it has indeed begun. And use should continue to be made, of course, of findings from the psychoanalyses of physicians, a special kind of reconstructive data from a special population using a unique tool—the analytic situation as an investigative opportunity.

At the other end of the temporal spectrum, the period of time displayed by the tiny space from points C through D in the diagrams—the whole of a professional lifetime—is just as urgently in need of study. In the area of graduate training, the first small portion of the space, Applebaum (1967), Menninger (1959), and Sutherland (1951), for example, have viewed residency training developmentally. These accounts are valuable and remarkable. They are also atypical; this sector of medical education has mostly been seen as training, and considerations of it are drained of attention to vital maturational features. The literature reveals no delineation of the first postgraduate medical years as a series of developmental stages, no proposals that this period might be thought of as a set of unfolding events, as well characterized by the terms used to describe growth as by the notions attached to learning. And there is certainly no sign of advance to a more sophisticated and objective position entertaining the possibility that both development and education might be vital components in a complete picture of the graduate training era, yet may not be its essence.

In some ways research in postgraduate medical education presents fewer obvious challenges in terms of data collection: Resident populations are generally housed in an institution and subscribe to a set of medical traditions which make them relatively accessible for study. While this should remain an additional and fertile area for retrospective studies, a stream of daily observational data are available during this period. It seems both paradox and waste that supervision and guidance in postgraduate medical training could, with planning, simultaneously generate information to serve the dual purposes of educational and developmental research. Yet rarely has the opportunity been seized. From a methodological standpoint, offsetting the advantages for such future research is the complexity of the interaction between developmental currents and the professionalization which at this point comes to occupy a very large proportion of the doctor's life-space and energy. In the study of medical students the search for adequate explanatory hypotheses is focused upon potential. In later stages of training, achievements become developmental milestones—the branching of the tree whose roots are the lines.

This discussion is largely limited to the understanding and evaluation of paracognitive development. The volume of studies documenting, often in excellent and detailed fashion, the acquisition of cognitive accomplishments and clinical skills during the period of residency is extremely valuable and indeed mandated at present in most Western countries. The lack of assessments of the underlying psychological maturational currents, as in the training of medical students, is acute. If available and adequately utilized, it might well be capable of advancing the attainment of skills and knowledge well beyond the points presently achieved at the time formal graduate studies come to a close. And there is every reason to guess that with depth of understanding, this experience could be more fun for all parties to the learning. When cognitive and paracognitive domains can be linked so that their strengths pull in the same direction, when they are not only joined, but operate in phase with one another, potentiation of learning is a reasonable hope and expectation. Such syntonic functioning often results in accelerated inner developments in the learner, observable in patterns of patient care, acquisition of skills, and perhaps even performance on written, licensure and specialty examinations.

The Tracking Function

Portions of the evaluative records of two medical students will serve to illustrate this way of using the lines. The most important point to be made about the data presented here is that they were part of responses to routine evaluative forms. The anecdotal faculty comments which will be quoted were in all cases elicited spontaneously by what the instructors felt was a reasonable academic request: documentation of and expansion upon their assessments of medical students' performance of clinical tasks. Having been asked to rate a student's work as outstanding, or satisfactory, or unsatisfactory they were also encouraged to give examples of behaviors that led to these judgments. The faculty reporters who authored the comments had no knowledge of the material presented in this manuscript except for the term *paracognitive,* which had been introduced to them in a memo that contained the diagram reproduced above as figure 1 and a definition of the term similar to that given in our glossary. The ideas put forward seemed poorly received, their meaning understood partially at best, and the whole project was more the target of good-humored jokes than serious consideration. The faculty raters were openly skeptical about the usefulness of the entity. To their everlasting credit and sense of fair play, the idea seemed to have been tried by most of them; many found it wanting and discarded it. Although technically naive with regard to the idea of developmental periods, perhaps faculty were intuitively using some internal framework similar to these to structure and select their comments. If indeed instructors were unconsciously using paracognitive dimensions, that might be one explanation for the heartening fact (for us) that the results could be used to affix tracking points on the developmental lines.

There should be no doubt or confusion on one point: Specific conceptual naiveté should not be interpreted to imply any hint of carelessness nor to suggest the absence of serious thought about the comments quoted below. This faculty group were acutely aware, as are most medical school faculties, of the importance of noncognitive factors in medical work. These factors were identified as habits, attitudes, or motivation and often equated with judgments based upon observable phenomena such as proper dress, respectful demeanor toward teachers or patients. But regardless of how they were conceptualized, these judgments could be used for tracking.

1. Student U

The most orderly way to illustrate this process is to present the faculty comments that were used as evidence for the location of points on the charts, moving from lines 1 through 5 sequentially. Figure 10 depicts Student U.

Line 1. Objectivity and Empathy. An instructor made this comment about Student U in the middle of his junior year as evidence for positive development in this dimension: "He came into my office very concerned about possible drug interaction of medications he had prescribed for one of his patients." But as an indication that mastery in this line was preceding less well in other ways at about the same time, another instructor wrote that in response to questions about content, the student "doesn't express himself well."

We digress here to justify the placement of this point and to submit evidence that we have not extrapolated or overinterpreted this brief statement. Surveillance of many medical student evaluations has made it apparent that in the condensed style of reporting used by most busy faculty members this kind of comment has a reliable psychological translation. A follow-up inquiry usually results in statements that the phrase is meant to convey a hunch or conviction that the student's grasp of the knowledge and the firm placement of it in an objective, quickly retrievable scan has not occurred. Inadequate expression is a result of the fact that the data have not been mastered or overlearned sufficiently.

Toward the end of his junior year, as evidence for above average development toward empathy and objectivity, there is the remark,

FIGURE 10

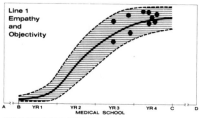

Line 1
Empathy
and
Objectivity

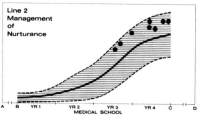

Line 2
Management
of
Nurturance

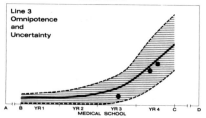

Line 3
Omnipotence
and
Uncertainty

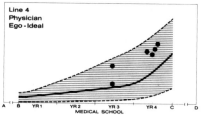

Line 4
Physician
Ego-Ideal

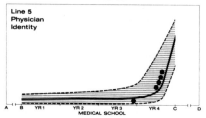

Line 5
Physician
Identity

"the student impressed me most when working with patients." And comments from the student's senior year include many which placed him above the line of maximum central tendency:

It was my feeling that the student was well aware of the effects of anxiety in life situations in this case.

Physical examination was accurate. He did recognize an S–4 "heart sound" but failed to hear a faint cardiac murmur known to be present. He formulated a good problem list. Chest x-ray was interpreted correctly. Electrocardiogram interpretation correctly identified the effects which digitalis might have upon the tracing. Student plan of management was a practical one. He was a little weak in his differential diagnosis of atrial fibrillation but did recognize that thyrotoxicosis and mitral stenosis were the two major associated diseases.

In pediatrics he appeared to have excellent knowledge of various topics. Worked well with patients.

Student has continued to show outstanding attitude toward primary care patient relationships.

Excellent clinical manner. Enthusiastic, knowledgeable.

Examples of comments made about two-thirds of the way through the student's senior year which chart near the line of average developmental progress include the following:

A hard worker—really tries to do a good job, but judgment is not based on solid knowledge grasp of the situation.

He is slow but thinks out his decisions and sticks to them.

Line 2. Management of Nurturance. The following comments attest to the fact that Student U's mastery in the management of nurturance was well above the customary levels in his junior year:

Came into my office very concerned about possible interaction of medications he prescribed for one of his patients.

This student is the only student who can really get control of the very demanding patient.

He seemed to be interested in being exposed to patients suffering proctological conditions—how they can be helped. He was kindly interested in them personally.

The following statements from his senior year account for the cluster of points indicating mastery well above expected levels:

Student impressed me most when working with patients.

It was my feeling that Student U was well aware of the effects of anxiety in life situations in this case.

In pediatrics he worked well with patients.

Student has continued to show outstanding attitude toward primary care patient relationships.

Excellent clinical manner. Enthusiastic. Will try to woo him to our medical school for residency.

This comment came from a faculty member at another hospital with whom the student had taken an independent study program: "He is very conscientious and at no time did I see him let down a patient, peer or other physicians."

Line 3. Omnipotence and Uncertainty. In this area Student U showed less outstanding mastery. From his junior year there is the comment: "Cooperative and attentive, but not as knowledgeable as the other students on this rotation. Not aggressive—a bit too quiet. Not anxious to offer any suggestions." The following comments illustrate his progress in the senior year:

Since his skills have improved so much here (on this service) he has shown more confidence with knowledge too.

Could not answer a very easy question regarding mechanism of action of drug. I believe he is weak in basic sciences.

His impaired capacity to express himself is a shortcoming. There is some hesitancy and incoherence in his reports, remarks and conversations. This may be due in part to a lack of medical knowledge or lack of confidence in his knowledge.

Student performed slowly after much deliberation. It is my feeling that he demonstrated very satisfactory performance in the practical handling of patient.

Needs to develop self-confidence.

Line 4. Physician Ego-Ideal. During his junior and senior year this student exhibited development in the physician ego-ideal which was above average. Comments during his junior year included:

Does his work well without complaint or question. Very adequate.

He seemed to be interested in the basic fundamentals of proctology and disturbed because insufficient didactic work had been provided in course [work in the medical school].

Came into my office very concerned about possible drug interaction of medications he prescribed for one of his patients. *Stayed until he got the answers.* [italics ours]

In his senior year, faculty commented:

On two occasions his scientific curiosity and perseverance contributed materially to the improvement of the patient. He is slow but thinks out his decisions and sticks to them.

Tries hard, very honest.

His strongest point is his personal desire to be thorough, complete and good at what he is doing.

Line 5. Physician Identity. In this area Student U's development followed very closely that of his peers. In his junior year: "Lackluster performance, but average to low." And then in his senior year:

He is slow but thinks out his decisions and sticks to them. He should prove to be a fine physician.

Compares favorably to his classmates in all categories, [knowledge, skills and attitudes] and is an excellent student and *physician.* His strongest point though is his personal desire to be thorough, complete and good at what he is doing. He is very conscientious and at no time did I see him let down a patient, peer or *other physicians*. He commands the respect of peers and teachers. [italics ours]

Summary. As Figure 10 suggests, this student's development in paracognitive areas was very near the median of his class, as were assessments of his progress from more conventional devices such as written examinations and clinical exercises. The reputation he enjoyed among faculty and students alike was best summarized by a classmate who said, "It's true he may not have been the most brilliant member of our class, but I can tell you this: If I were ever traveling in the part of the country where I know he means to practice, I would go to him for medical care for myself and my family, and that, with perfect trust."

2. *Student V*

As Figure 11 shows, comments about this student indicated he was consistently near the upper limits of educational feasibility.

Line 1. Objectivity and Empathy. An instructor commented about him in his junior year: "Exceptional student, has good bedside manner." In his senior year he was described as:

Well focused.

The best student I've had overall. Excellent data base. He is accurate and intellectually honest. He is quiet to a fault, but when he speaks it is with accuracy and precision. He reads constantly.

His base of knowledge is excellent and he works toward improving it. His skills are satisfactory and they were improving steadily on the rotation.

He presented his material in a concise, organized fashion. History and physical examination were good and well done. The history was somewhat vague but this was primarily because of the patient's inability to provide the detailed information due to a mild organic brain syndrome. His discussion of the case and workup appeared very adequate and he did an unusually good job in ordering laboratory work and getting to the problem.

His base of knowledge was exceptional.

FIGURE 11

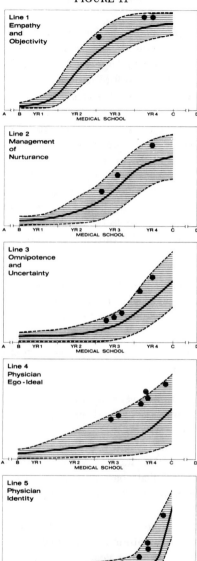

Line 2. The Management of Nurturance. Early in his junior year, instructors commented: "he is a kind, considerate young man." "[He]... has good bedside manner." In his senior year it was noted that "he relates well to patients."

Line 3. Omnipotence and Uncertainty. The following comments enabled estimates of progress at the upper edges of educational feasibility. In the middle of his junior year the student "asked that a program be set up to bring him up to date on more drugs other than those used in gastroenterology [the rotation upon which the instructor was reporting]." A faculty member reported: "He will on occasion be reluctant to speak up with an opinion for fear of being wrong. He is knowledgeable. He is methodical to the point where he might appear to be 'dragging his heels' but he gets things done adequately." Also during the junior year, the following reports were received:

Without prompting he undertook a library review of a topic I only mentioned in passing and displayed a knowledge of the entity far beyond mine within twenty-four hours of discussing the topic. Reads voluntarily. Conscientious.

He was prompted to ask questions and pursue areas of learning that were prompted by patient problems.

In the student's senior year, an instructor recorded his performance on an examination focused on a specific case: "During the discussion, he was somewhat vague in a few areas, specifically the discussion of anemia associated with liver disease, but he corrected himself after some false starts." Midway through the year the comment was made: "Data base appeared unusually good and his ability to synthesize information was excellent. Overall impression was outstanding."

Line 4. Physician Ego-Ideal. In this area of development the pattern of excellence for Student V was documented by the following comments from his junior year:

Asked that a program be set up to bring himself up to date on more drugs other than gastroenterology [the rotation upon which the instructor was reporting]. *Often* asks questions privately. [italics instructor's]

He is a personable, interested student who related very well to the patients. It was a pleasure to have him participate [in the care of patients in the office setting].

The following comments illustrate placement of data points in the senior year:

I found him easy to work with.

His base of knowledge is excellent and he works toward improving it. His skills are satisfactory and they were improving steadily on this rotation. His habits and attitudes are satisfactory plus.

On the whole he appeared poised throughout the examination, [an individual oral examination on a specifically selected case in medicine, and] showed no evidence of undue anxiety. Was able to respond to questions well.

His base of knowledge was exceptional and his dedication to medicine is outstanding. He has shown constant improvement throughout his student experience.

Line 5. Physician Identity. An instructor wrote of him early in his junior year, "He should make a fine physician." And during the first month of his senior year: "This student is a very capable student-physician and I enjoyed participating with him in his clinical exposure to pediatrics. Very capable student-physician." Other comments from the senior year included:

Developing steadily.

Needs to learn how to project his personality more. [Note that this comment represents the point located on figure 11 nearest the line of median development.]

On the whole he appeared poised throughout the examination, showed no evidence of undue anxiety, was able to respond to questions well.

His base of knowledge was exceptional and his dedication to medicine is outstanding. He has shown constant improvement throughout his student experience.

Summary.   Student V, like Student U, was well regarded by his classmates. His paracognitive development, clearly at the upper ranges of what we have defined as expectable, was reflected by superior performance on more conventional assessment devices, and his graduation was accompanied by honors and awards.

These examples can serve to illustrate issues relevant to more general considerations for measurement. Among the most important is the fact that the translocation from the instructor's comments to points on a graph involves several stages of inferential reasoning, and a rationale for these is essential. All of the placements were made by one judge. The fact that his location of progress points might differ from other judges emphasizes and illustrates one essential step and obvious research effort necessary before actually using these scales. Initial steps such as comparison of a number of judges' data, analysis of the variability of point placements, and the recording of the judges' rationale for the location would be some of a number of obligatory and, for the most part well worked out procedures available for transforming theoretical and graphically represented concepts such as those we have presented into acceptable measurements.

The rationale could be presented here for the location of each data point on figures 10 and 11, but there are two additional reasons to spare the reader this exegesis. (1) If the explanation of the network of lines of development in preceding chapters has been even partially successful, much of the reasoning should suggest itself. (2) As an exercise in self-assessment or for more active participation in learning, the venturesome may wish to reread the comments and locate their own data points on the graph. For the practice to be most effective, each placement must be accompanied by a rationale. It might be related either to the theoretical notions proposed earlier or evoked by responses to them or suggested by totally new ideas, but the logical link may not be arbitrary, impressionistic, or inexplicit.

The two students chosen as illustrations for this section were deliberately selected because developmental progress was relatively similar: These students' evaluative records (less than 15 percent of the material has been presented here) were replete with affirmations from faculty that both would be good physicians. Toward the close of their undergraduate training both were carrying large amounts of autonomous clinical responsibility for patient care and doing this well. Both were respected by faculty colleagues, peers, and health-care teammates of many disciplines. The choice of two individuals of relative developmental similarity to demonstrate the tracking function was based on the fact that in order to perform this function adequately, the lines must demonstrate a capacity to discriminate with some accuracy and to do so with judgments (admittedly inferential) based upon realistic, in this case anecdotal, data.

The fact that a number of statements have served as location points on several scales fits with emphases made earlier. The task of disentangling the lines from a developmental gestalt, of attempting to estimate overlap between them and identify both instances of co-occurrence and the variance mutually accounted for by each, has been a large part of this endeavor. Recombining the braided and intermixed currents and mapping the reassembly has been a second thrust. Neither of the examples of these two tasks put forward here are advanced as complete, nor is it our expectation that conversions of data points to locations on the graph are as precise as we hope to make them eventually. The purpose of this section was to test whether the capacity for unidimensional patterning was sufficient to permit tracking with the lines in their present state of evolution. Figures 10 and 11 suggest that it can be done well enough to be of some usefulness and that the method has enough promise to warrant further investigation.

Mapping: Another Dimension for the Judgments

In tracking, an individual's development is charted over time relative to a designated criterion range, permitting comparisons between measures of his own performance and those of normative groups. The lines of development can also be used to capture a picture of development much in the way a single frame or still photograph might augment moving pictures, allowing closer study of detail. The shaded areas shown as swaths of educational feasibility in figures 10 and 11 also indicate calculated estimates of variance: We posit the 67 percent of developmental events for each line fall between the upper- and lowermost lines in all the graphs. This figure encompasses the range of one standard deviation above and below the measure of most central tendency.

Figure 12 is designed to demonstrate the use of the lines of development as probability estimates and the expansion of two-dimensional swaths to allow representation of data from a number of judges. The graph also is an effort to allow more adequate depiction of the panoply of comments which result from thoughtful assessment of clinical performance and paracognitive progress, in whatever manner it is obtained—anecdotes, numbers, grades, or all of these. The assignment of one data point for each of the comments listed for figures 10 and 11 is tolerable for tracking purposes. But such a procedure results in substantial condensation, and its lack of depth and failure to make full use of the data as information are a serious waste.

One way to restore a more complete feel of and for the comments is the use of the lines for a single time-slice. In an effort to show how this method might work, Student W's performance is depicted in figure 12. The comments charted cover his performance within a three-week period early in his senior year in medical school. Placed in the two-dimensional tracking or monitoring mode, they would cluster very closely at a location above the median developmental trend, but within the 34 percent of incidents between that midpoint and the edge we have posited as educationally feasible. This situation is as shown in the upper part of the figure.

If, however, one imagines that the area shown as the line XY in the upper graph is, in addition, a slice which could be extracted and turned ninety degrees for viewing, the result is the graph

FIGURE 12

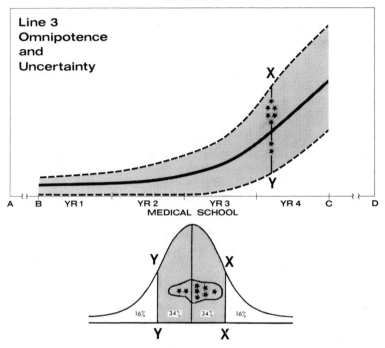

shown in the lower portion of figure 12. An alternative way to visualize this idea is to imagine that the shaded portion of the upper graph might be folded over the line of most central tendency into the shape in lower graph. That shape, familiar to most students, educators, and statisticians, was chosen because it has been demonstrated that a very large number of measures of natural phenomena, from agricultural productivity to moral judgments, if collected in sufficient numbers will distribute themselves in this manner. For the curious, the rationale, uses, and importance of this fact, known technically as the Central Limits Theorem, can be found in many statistics texts (Frank 1974 pp. 213–14; Minium 1970, pp. 227–28). We believe that inspection of such materials will convince most readers that this distribution is the best first guess about how paracognitive ratings will be distributed.

The comments made by instructors about Student W during this brief time were as follows:

I did not have much exposure to this student, but what I did see was consistently high quality. He needs more specific information. He will spend additional time with me on an elective basis during which time we will see how he works under pressure.

He is extremely well motivated. He had reviewed all the textbook and audio-visual material available prior to entering the rotation. He had mastered the basic examinations' skills as well. During the time that he was with me, he was polishing the skills he had already developed himself. His attitudes are superior, his ability to arrive at a diagnosis and the implication of the diagnosis was again superior.

His overall performance was good to excellent, he did competent histories and physicals with no significant defects noted. He was vague on various aspects of patient management, specificially in diabetes. He performed quite inadequately both in managing an actual case and subsequently in presenting that patient to me during a case presentation. During an oral examination he showed serious deficits and attempted to talk his way out of some questions that were asked and his answers were completely inappropriate and inaccurate. Dr. X [another preceptor] and I noted a tendency to talk without thinking and to give erroneous information on occasion. It would be my recommendation that future instructors watch this young man for these tendencies because on the whole he is a very competent and bright student. He has a good data base and can formulate ideas from specific facts and construct an adequate problem list. However, effort should be made to make sure that information he is giving is correct and where this is not the case he must be held accountable for misinformation.

Student W indicated that he was capable of performing an adequate history and physical examination. He readily grasped the diagnosis [hyperthyroidism]. He showed, however, serious defects in terms of treatment and his treatment plan was vague. He indicated by this maneuver either an inability to recognize his own weaknesses or the fact that he was honestly mistaken and thought he was giving correct information.

The student made a good presentation. He was somewhat nervous, but this did not detract from it. He exhibited a good fund of knowledge and much to my surprise and delight included pheochromocytoma in a differential diagnosis of the thryotoxicosis.

The last three comments were independent reports submitted by three faculty members present at the same assessment exercise.

Note that the lower diagram on figure 12 permits the mapping of positive comments about attitude, motivation, and prior study as these are seen as relevant to the mastery of omnipotence and uncertainty. It also accommodates remarks about the student's deficits—his uncertainty about what he knew, his inability to recognize what he did not know, his difficulty in admitting his ignorance to the faculty, and his problems in mastering the affects such an admission must evoke, especially in a senior medical student. These are shown as points below the central tendency.

Student W was known as someone who could indeed be ingratiating, but he had a reputation for being glib, of giving the impression of mastery when in fact his grasp of content was tenuous and his coherent integration of data, flimsy. At a time when development in handling the longings for omnipotence, the necessity for adequate knowledge, and the imperative of recognizing the limits of uncertainty ought to have been under good management, this student had not progressed as far as, in the words of a faculty member, one would hope a senior student should.

The comments clearly show two points of interest for our theses. First, the time-slice approach can show the variability with which faculty were able to perceive this situation—some were taken in by the student's facade while others, perhaps probing more deeply or having the occasion to observe in a more fortunate and intense situation, were not. Second, the data demonstrate that a student falling below the expected paracognitive development in some ways can be identified by these methods even if the judgment is a difficult one. Once detected (or perhaps one might say diagnosed) a student showing developmental lags should receive prompt help in shoring up cognitive as well as paracognitive support systems. Indeed, some of the comments of the instructors indicate how they thought this might be done.

Measurement in Depth: Refinement of a Technique

Before going further let us review the uses suggested thus far for the lines of development. They can be used to compare assessments of a given individual over time. They can also be used as a frame within which probabilities can be estimated, allowing the comparison of the individual to a number of groups, or a series of groups to one another. For example, a student can be compared to groups of students at similar points in training in his own year in the medical school he is attending, to students of comparable years in the country in which he is training, or to temporally disparate groups. Sophomore medical students can be compared to residents, or to those who have completed premedical studies, been admitted to medical school but not yet matriculated. Temporally disparate group comparisons offer the beginning of quantification estimates and parameters from which might evolve predictive estimates.

All of these possibilities spring from use of the lines of development in the tracking function—a two-dimensional enterprise.

The lines can also be used for mapping. The procedures involved provide for fuller utilization of variations in the depth of judgments, for evaluation of differences in the skills with which the judgments are made, and for quantification and processing of the larger numbers of ratings needed to increase reliability and approach validity. All of the functions suggested earlier for tracking can still be accomplished, but in addition, probability estimates attached to these measures enhance and expand the kind of tracking that can be done. Detection of difficulties is possible sooner and with more accuracy, as in the case of Student W. The increased scope and precision of the data will encourage modes of thinking about developmental problems which are conducive to the establishment of rating systems that can signal the location of any given individual rating for the rater or the object of his judgment. Thus a faculty member or a student could be supplied information about the direction and course of developmental progress, the rate at which it is proceeding, and an estimate of the chances of spontaneous changes in direction. Armed with more complete understanding of this sort, we can estimate the consequences of intervention in development. Specifically, remedial or enrichment programs can be based on better estimates of their chances of success and monitored as they are implemented. Routes leading toward the integration of cognitive and paracognitive processes—another goal of this work— become more accessible. These are some of the results of a three-dimensional approach.

Figure 13 is meant to suggest that an even better approximation of the intricacy of the phenomenon we are describing is possible if it is thought of in three dimensions. This model no more captures truly the feeling of multidimensionality than any others; but we hope that the distortions necessary for clarity in expansion are not severe enough to obscure the basic concepts and that

FIGURE 13

corrections can be introduced in time. The probability spaces in the figure are an arrangement of expansions of the three-dimensional framework used as an illustration for mapping. If a large series of time slices like the one illustrated in the lower graph in figure 12 were stacked together, the result would be the shape labeled line 3. Each of the spaces has as a crest the line of maximum central tendency hypothesized for that line. The outlines of the curves for lines 1 and 5, identical to those diagrammed in figures 3 and 7, can be seen most readily. The bulk around these crests corresponds to the variance hypothesized for each line. In the two-dimensional version this is the shaded portion above and below the line. An essential point is that wherever the spaces might be intersected by a plane placed perpendicular to the line of greatest frequency, the resulting slice would reveal a distribution embodied in the axioms of the Central Limits Theorem.

It is at the point where the spaces begin to merge that we must ask the most from the reader's imagination and patience. We need more data before the dissection and description of this area can begin. Having emerged from a developmental view, however, the similarity of the diagram (at least superficially) to the roots of a tree will perhaps not seem excessively allegorical. The true state of affairs would be much better captured by a photograph of a real tree trunk. Its jumble of interlocking tendrils would be less tidy and more valid than our careful, artificially arranged spaces, but the resemblance suggests that both the diagrammatic and photographic depictions have value and might eventually converge.

Before us remain the tasks of filling in the curves, variabilities, and shapes between points A and B, and C and D, in our graphing of the line of development. These can also be encompassed by the arboreal analogy. The bases from which the shapes in figure 13 arise, the soil characteristics necessary for the roots, have yet to be described; so, also, do the results of the root growth, for example, vascular patterns which yield differing trunk sizes leading to variations in branching, function, size, and longevity of the tree. Without belaboring the matter, there is no shortage of work to be done, of riddles to be solved, or of mysteries to be cleared up.

The transition from the grace and fluidity of the world of ideas to the arena of painstaking, slowly built implementation is a wrenching one. To ease this process we want to persuade readers that the different kind of challenge one encounters in application is no less exciting because its strategies are different. We therefore close with a kind of coda—a combination of promissory notes and a reminder list. It is meant to pluck at the sleeve of the reader's mind and to record for our conscience' sake and his encouragement that many discoveries are still before us. Much of the business begun here remains unfinished.

What has been served up in this setting is an aperitif, meant to prepare and whet the appetite, but not satisfy it. Readers are entitled at least to some clues about the main bill of fare. Among the many questions which clamor for attention are those hovering around the enigma of how differently doctors turn out and how much of this variation could be explained by what we have proposed. And apart from our curiosity about the development of individual doctors we need to investigate doctors in working groups, from two-person partnerships through large medical centers, on to private megaclinics and the super-megaclinics like the Mayo, for example. Another issue is the extent to which our ideas about professional development may affect physicians, their family and personal relationships. Adequate studies of doctors' wives and children, for example, might contain much evidence relevant to our hypotheses and would be interesting in their own right.

When the answers to these puzzles—some best approached by analogy, some by observation, some accessible only by inference—are within the range of our understanding, perhaps a level of knowledge will be achieved which will finally allay our puzzlement and curiosity. At this point in our studies, satiety seems a long way off.

Bibliography

Appelbaum, S. A. 1967. The pleasure and reality principles in group process teaching. *British Journal of Medical Psychology* 36: 49–56.

Association of American Medical Colleges, Division of Educational Measures and Research. January, 1975. Medical college admission tests. 1974 summary of score distribution.

Balint, M. 1964. *The doctor, his patient and the illness.* 2nd ed. London: Pitman.

Becker, H. S.; Geer, B.; Hughes, E. C.; and Straus, A. L. 1961. *Boys in white.* Chicago: University of Chicago Press.

Bruner, J. S. 1960. *The process of education.* Cambridge, Mass.: Harvard University Press.

Bynder, H. 1965. Physicians choose psychiatrists: medical social structure and patterns of choice. *Journal of Health and Human Behavior* 6:83–91.

Caldwell, B. M. 1968. The usefulness of the critical period hypothesis in the study of filiative behavior. In *Contemporary issues in developmental psychology,* ed. N. S. Endler, L. R. Boulter, H. Osser, pp. 213–33. New York: Holt, Rinehart and Winston.

Clyne, M. B. 1963. *Night calls.* London: Tavistock.

DeLevita, D. L. 1976. On the psychoanalytic concept of identity. *International Journal of Psychoanalysis* 47:2–3.

Denenberg, V. H. 1968. Critical periods, stimulus input and emotional reactivity: a theory of infantile stimulation. In *Contemporary issues in developmental psychology,* ed. N. S. Endler, L. R. Boulter, H. Osser, pp. 198–213. New York: Holt, Rinehart and Winston.

Endler, N. S.; Boulter, L. R.; and Osser, H., eds. 1968. *Contemporary issues in developmental psychology.* New York: Holt, Rinehart and Winston.

Erikson, E. H. 1950. *Childhood and society.* New York: Norton.

———. 1958. *Young man Luther.* New York: Norton.

———. 1959. *Identity and the life cycle.* Psychological Issues Monographs, vol. 1, no. 1. New York: International Universities Press.

———. 1975. *Life history and the historical moment.* New York: Norton.

171

Fitch, E. M. 1964. Referral to the psychiatrist in an American view. *Med. World* 100:499–504.

Frank, H. 1974. *Introduction to probability and statistics: concepts and principles.* New York: Wiley.

Fredericks, M. A., and Mundy, P. 1976. *The making of a physician.* Chicago: Loyola University Press.

Freud, A. 1958. The theory of parent-infant relationships. *International Journal of Psychoanalysis* 13:92–116.

———. 1965. *Normality and pathology in childhood.* New York: International Universities Press.

Freud, S. 1905, 1953. [*Three contributions to a theory of sexuality.*] Hogarth Standard Edition 7:125–44. London: Hogarth Press.

Glauber, P. I. 1953. A deterrent in the study and practice of medicine. *Psychoanalytic Quarterly* 22:381–412.

Greco, R., and Pittenger, R. 1966. *One man's practice.* New York: Lippincott.

Harlow, H. S. 1968. The heterosexual affectional system in monkeys. In *Contemporary issues in developmental psychology,* ed. N. S. Endler, L. R. Boulter, H. Osser, pp. 156–63. New York: Holt, Rinehart and Winston.

Hess, E. H. Imprinting in birds. In *Contemporary issues in developmental psychology,* ed. N. S. Endler, L. R. Boulter, H. Osser, pp. 163–80. New York: Holt, Rinehart and Winston.

Howe, I. 1976. *World of our fathers.* New York: Harcourt, Brace, Jovanovich.

Kernberg, O. 1974. Mature love: prerequisites and characteristics. *Journal of the American Psychoanalytic Association* 22:743–63.

Kestenberg, J. 1961. Menarche. In *Adolescents: psychoanalytic approach to problems and therapy,* ed. S. Lorand and H. I. Schneer, pp. 19–50. New York: P. B. Hoeber.

Knight, J. A. 1973. *Medical student.* New York: Appleton-Century-Crofts.

Kohut, H. 1971. *The analysis of the self: a systematic approach to the psychoanalytic treatment of narcissistic personality disorder.* New York: International Universities Press.

Kudlien, F. 1970. Medical education in classical antiquity. In *The history of medical education,* ed. C. D. O'Malley, pp. 3–37. Berkeley and Los Angeles: University of California Press.

Kuhn, T. S. 1962. *The structure of scientific revolutions.* Chicago: University of Chicago Press.

Lewin, B. D. 1946. Counter-transference in the technique of medical practice. *Psychosomatic Medicine* 8:195–99.

McLaughlin, J. T. 1961. The analyst and the Hippocratic oath. *Journal of the American Psychoanalytic Association* 9:106–23.

Mahler, M. S. 1968. *On human symbiosis and the vicissitudes of individuation.* New York: International Universities Press.

Menninger, K. A. 1959. Psychological factors in the choice of medicine as a profession. In *A psychiatrist's world: selected papers*, ed. Bernard H. Fall, pp. 477–96. New York: Viking Press.

Minium, E. R. 1970. *Statistical reasoning in psychology and education.* New York: Wiley.

Moore, B. E., and Fine, B. D., eds. 1968. *A glossary of psychoanalytic terms and concepts.* 2nd. ed. New York: American Psychoanalytic Association.

Nunberg, H. 1938. Psychological interrelations between physician and patient. *Psychoanalytic Review* 25:197–308.

O'Malley, C. D. 1970. *The history of medical education.* Berkeley and Los Angeles: University of California Press.

Piaget, J. 1954. *The child's conception of reality.* New York: Basic Books.

Rapaport, D. 1957. *Cognitive structures: contemporary approaches to cognition.* Cambridge, Mass.: Harvard University Press.

Rezler, A. G. 1974. Attitude changes during medical school: a review of the literature. *Journal of Medical Education* 49:1023–30.

Rose, J. C. 1974. Who will teach the basic medical sciences? *Science* 185:1022–27.

Scott, J. P. 1968. Critical periods in behavioral development. In *Contemporary issues in developmental psychology,* ed. N. S. Endler, L. R. Boulter, H. Osser, pp. 181–97. New York: Holt, Rinehart and Winston.

Shevrin, H. 1976. Rapaport's contribution to research: a look to the future. Paper presented to the Chicago Psychoanalytic Society, 25 May 1976, p. 2.

Simmel, E. 1926. The 'doctor-game': illness and the profession in medicine. *International Journal of Psychoanalysis* 7:470–83.

Singer, J. D. 1972. *Boundaries of the soul.* New York: Doubleday.

Spitz, R. A. (with the assistance of K. M. Wolf). 1946. *The smiling response.* Genetic Psychology Monographs, no. 34.

Sutherland, R. L. 1951. An application of the theory of psychosexual development to the learning process. *Bulletin of the Menninger Clinic* 15:91–99.

Zabarenko, L. M.; Pittenger, R. A.; and Zabarenko, R. N. 1968. *Primary medical practice.* St. Louis: Warren Green.

Zabarenko, L. M., and Zabarenko, R. N. 1974. Psychoanalytic contributions for a theory of instruction. *Annual of Psychoanalysis* 2:323–45.

Zabarenko, R. N.; Zabarenko, L. M.; and Pittenger, R. A. 1970. The psychodynamics of physicianhood. *Psychiatry* 33:102–18.

Zakon, S. F. N.d. *Religio medici.* New York: Sheffer Printing Corp.

Contemporary Community Health Series

HEALTH CARE IN THE EUROPEAN COMMUNITY
Alan Maynard

HOME TREATMENT
Spearhead of Community Psychiatry
Leonard Weiner, Alvin Becker, and Tobias T. Friedman

LONG-TERM CHILDHOOD ILLNESS
Harry A. Sultz, Edward R. Schlesinger, William E. Mosher, and Joseph G. Feldman

MARRIAGE AND MENTAL HANDICAP
A Study of Subnormality in Marriage
Janet Mattinson

A METHOD OF HOSPITAL UTILIZATION REVIEW
Sidney Shindell and Morris London

METHODOLOGY IN EVALUATING THE QUALITY OF MEDICAL CARE
An Annotated Selected Bibliography, 1955–1968
Isidore Altman, Alice J. Anderson, and Kathleen Barker
Out of print

MIGRANTS AND MALARIA IN AFRICA
R. Mansell Prothero
Out or print

THE PSYCHIATRIC HALFWAY HOUSE
A Handbook of Theory and Practice
Richard D. Budson

A PSYCHIATRIC RECORD MANUAL FOR THE HOSPITAL
Dorothy Smith Keller

RACISM AND MENTAL HEALTH
Charles V. Willie, Bernard M. Kramer, and Bertram S. Brown, Editors

SOCIAL SKILLS AND MENTAL HEALTH
Peter Trower, Bridget Bryant, and Michael Argyle

THE SOCIOLOGY OF PHYSICAL DISABILITY AND REHABILITATION
Gary L. Albrecht, Editor

THE STYLE AND MANAGEMENT OF A PEDIATRIC PRACTICE
Lee W. Bass and Jerome H. Wolfson